ANDERSON UNIVERSITY
PR4825.J3 P3 1910 ¢58552!
INAN
Jerome / The
floor back : an
3 2197 00093 1846

D1112684

"I shall not be able to go to-night."

Frontispiece]

[See p. 88.

THE PASSING OF THE THIRD FLOOR BACK

AN IDLE FANCY

IN A PROLOGUE, A PLAY, AND AN EPILOGUE

BY

JEROME K. JEROME

"I will seek thy good"

LONDON
HURST & BLACKETT, LTD.
PATERNOSTER HOUSE, E.C.

PRINTED IN GREAT BRITAIN
BY HAZELL, WATSON AND VINEY, LD.,
LONDON AND AYLESBURY.

CHARACTERS IN THE PROLOGUE

A Satyr
A Coward
A Bully
A Shrew
A Hussy
A Rogue
A Cad
A Cat
A Snob
A Slut
A Cheat
and
A Passer-by

The Passing of the Third Floor Back

PROLOGUE

SCENE

The first floor front of 13, *Bloomsbury Place, London, W.C. The furniture is of the Early Victorian or horsehair period. A worn Brussels carpet covers the floor. A large round table occupies the centre of the room. The high bay windows, looking out upon the street, are draped with red curtains; between them stands a small desk. Against the wall at back, an old-fashioned cottage piano, and a sideboard. From the wall to the right of the audience large folding doors lead into the dining-room. Two easy-chairs face the fire, which is supposed to be in front: a dull red glow spreads itself across the room. The door at back opens into the passage. Opposite to it is the front door, surmounted by a "fanlight"; and beyond, the ever-misty square, leafless in winter dreariness. A heavy three-branched gaselier hangs from the ceiling, the globes hidden under paper shades.*

It is a Friday afternoon in November.

[MRS. SHARPE *is making out her bills. She is a tall, thin, sharp-featured woman. She wears a widow's cap and spectacles; the latter she takes off when not writing. She looks up from her writing, looks at her watch, then calls.*]

MRS. SHARPE

Stasia! [*She rises and goes to the door.*] Lazy hussy. [*Calls louder*] Stasia!

STASIA

[*Without.*] All right—all right. Don't shout. Spoil yer voice for singing.

[*Enter as she speaks* STASIA, *carrying a tray laden with tea-things. She is a slatternly young person, her hair fluffed all about her head.*]

MRS. SHARPE

Don't answer me like that, you workhouse brat you. What have you been doing?

STASIA

Injoring myself. [*Puts down the tray on the table.*] All there is to do in this plice.

MRS. SHARPE

You take care you don't lose it—find yourself with the key of the street in your pocket. Not many places open to girls just out of prison.

STASIA

Industrial school, if you please.

MRS. SHARPE

[*Gives a snorting laugh.*] What time did old Wright come in last night?

STASIA

[*She is laying the table.*] 'Bout 'alf past 'leven or quarter to twelve.

MRS. SHARPE

Drunk?

STASIA

Oh, just fuddled, sime as usual. You know, I suppose, that ye're out of whiskey?

MRS. SHARPE

I'd forgotten it.

STASIA

Lucky 'e wasn't in a noticing mood. I give 'im 'alf a tumblerful of cold tea and filled it up with soda water. 'E went to bed singing. [*Laughs.*]

MRS. SHARPE

[*Thinking aloud.*] Cold tea ? Not a bad idea, that. Much the same colour.

STASIA

And less 'armful.

MRS. SHARPE

[*She grows confidential.*] He's the only one that ever asks for whiskey ?

STASIA

Only one of 'em as I'd trust not to blackmail yer afterwards for selling it to them without a licence.

MRS. SHARPE

No need to let him have it when he's sober You can have mislaid the key. Understand ?

STASIA

I understand. And where do I come in ?

MRS. SHARPE

You be a good girl, and maybe I'll find a blouse I've done with, when I've time to go over my drawer.

STASIA

Rather 'ave it 'fore you've done with it, if ye're sure yer can spare it. Don't want to be mistook, when I go out, for a bit of old London.

MRS. SHARPE

We'll see about it. Perhaps—— [*On her way back to the desk she has drifted near to the piano.*] Who's been burning these candles? They are two inches shorter than when I blew them out last night—that I'll swear.

STASIA

Nobody been in 'ere as I know of.

MRS. SHARPE

The tricks and the dodges that they're up to! It's like living in a den of lions. [*She has whipped out the candles, and with a pair of scissors is making secret marks upon them; which done, she replaces them.*]

STASIA

It's a rummy world when you come to think of it. [*Cheerfully*] Got to be doing somebody or being done from the time you get up in the morning until yer goes to bed at night. And when yer do fall asleep, it's to dream you've forgotten to bolt yer door. By the by, what about that third floor back? Ain't yer going to do anything?

MRS. SHARPE

Oh! I've spent more than I'll get out of it in a month, advertising it.

STASIA

You don't make 'em spicy enough. [*She takes up a folded copy of* "*The Christian World.*"] This is the sort of thing you want. [*Reads*] "To the lonely: all the joys of 'ome."

MRS. SHARPE

Yes, I tried that one—once. Told me with tears in his eyes that I reminded him of his mother, and went off before five o'clock the next morning with the drawing-room clock.

STASIA

'Ow about a card? That don't cost you nothing.

MRS. SHARPE

Don't quite like the idea of a card. Inviting all the rag-tag and bob-tail of the street to come into your house, it always seems to me like. Never know who may knock at your door.

STASIA

Maybe the very one you're waiting for. Was reading a story only the other d'y. A young girl—just in a spirit of fun like—puts up a card in the window, and a young man comes along, and just for the joke of it they take 'im in, and 'e turns out to be a nobleman—in disguise.

MRS. SHARPE

Yes, I can believe in the disguise. No; I don't like the idea of a card. We'll keep the house respectable so long as we can. [*With her bills in her hand she is passing out. She pauses to examine the milk-jug.*] I think, Stasia, the milk will bear a little more water. [*She goes out by the folding-doors.*]

STASIA

[*Mimics.*] "Don't quite like the idea of a card." Silly old fool! Don't know her own business.

[STASIA *thinks. She makes sure that* MRS. SHARPE *is out of sight; then takes a card from the drawer of the desk: with a chair goes out into the passage, climbs up and places the card in the fanlight over the front door. Returns. A beam of sunlight has softly stolen through the dingy fanlight. It lies across the room, growing in brightness.* STASIA *returning, after having replaced the chair, stops puzzled for a moment—sunbeams in Bloomsbury in November being rare.*]

Gorblimy, if it ain't the sun! [*She smiles.*] Forgotten all about 'im!

[*Then fetches a jug of water from the sideboard. Is about to fill up the milk-jug; pauses; looks round. Takes a long pull from the jug first. Then fills it up and replaces the water-jug. She goes out.*]

[*The front door is opened with a latchkey and* MISS KITE *enters. She is a maiden lady of forty; her ambition is to appear nineteen. She is painted and powdered and frizzled and beribboned. She wears fluffy golden hair, has pencilled eyebrows, made-up eyelashes, and carmine lips, with a waist of twenty-two. She giggles and gushes and simpers and bridles; and whenever she thinks nobody sees, is with the help of a pocket-mirror and toilet-case for ever powdering and patching herself.*]

MISS KITE

[*She looks in, sees the room is empty, enters. Opening her reticule, she takes out four candle ends, substitutes them for the half-burnt piano candles. This is done swiftly and neatly. Hearing footsteps, she slips out, closing the door softly behind her.*]

[*Re-enter* MRS. SHARPE *with a teapot. She puts down the teapot on the table; taking the key from her pocket, opens the tantalus on the sideboard, brings down the whiskey decanter and proceeds to fill it from the teapot. Holding it up to judge of the colour, she catches sight of the changed candles. She puts down the whiskey decanter and charges across the room; examines them—but of course they could not be the same. She is standing with them in her hand when re-enter Stasia, with remainder of tea-things, including large teapot.*]

MRS. SHARPE

Who's been in here?

STASIA

Nobody.

MRS. SHARPE

What's the good of telling lies?

STASIA

Who's telling lies? Think everybody's like yourself? Can't open their mouth——

MRS. SHARPE

Somebody must have been here. Candles don't change themselves. I'm——

[*Re-enter* MISS KITE, *having taken off her cloak and hat. A silence.*]

You haven't any idea, I presume, Miss Kite, who has been in here stealing the candles?

MISS KITE

Stealing the candles!

MRS. SHARPE

I beg their pardon. I should say "exchanging." That's no robbery, of course. [*From mock polite-*

ness to sudden fierceness] Taking four of them measuring well over six inches each, leaving me a set of measly stumps. [*Rams them back into their sockets.*] Nice sort of people living in this house, I must say.

MISS KITE

[*The tell-tale teapot with the unstoppered whiskey decanter beside it, remains on the table.* MISS KITE *sniffs expressively.*] Yes, do seem to be a bit tricky, some of them, don't they ?

MRS. SHARPE

[*She savagely puts back the decanter. To* STASIA] Don't stand there grinning, you slatternly monkey. Pull up your stockings, do ; and ring the tea-bell.

[*She gives her the cold teapot, and* STASIA *goes out. The bell is heard. A loud, brutal-sounding bell.*]

MISS KITE

Shouldn't be surprised, between ourselves, if it wasn't that girl Stasia. Tell you what I saw her doing only the other day——

[*There enters* MRS. MAJOR TOMPKINS. *She is plump, pretty, forty-five, with white hair.*]

Oh, good afternoon, dear Mrs. Tompkins.

[MRS. TOMPKINS *and* MRS. SHARPE *exchange a "Good afternoon." They seat themselves.*]

MISS KITE

And how is the dear Major? I thought he seemed a little "liverish" this morning.

MRS. TOMPKINS

Always is after dining out—at somebody else's expense. [*She laughs.*] Never can resist the temptation of over-eating himself.

MISS KITE

Poor man! Doesn't often get the opportunity, does he? Dear Mrs. Sharpe sees to that. [*She giggles.*] Only my little joke, dear.

MRS. SHARPE

A generous table I have always advertised, and a generous table it will always be my endeavour to maintain. Of course, if people will tight-lace so that their food can't——

MISS KITE

Not too much *cream*, dear, thank you.

MRS. SHARPE

[*Examines the milk.*] It *does* look a bit thin.

Shall really have to change my milkman—if this goes on.

MISS KITE

Tradesmen are such thieves! [*She winks at* MRS. TOMPKINS.] Isn't Mrs. Dooley—I beg her pardon, Mrs. de Hooley—going to honour us with her presence this afternoon?

MRS. TOMPKINS

Perhaps we are not good enough company for the cousin of a baronet. [*Laughs.*]

MISS KITE

Perhaps not. But I think we might be for the widow of a potato salesman. My dear, I know it for a fact. And oh, her meanness! Would you believe it, her own sister, her own nephews and nieces, starving: literally——

[MRS. DE HOOLEY *has entered, a large, flabby, pale-faced lady. She speaks with the accent of aristocratic languor.* MRS. SHARPE *has given a warning "Hush!"*]

We were just talking about you, dear. So afraid you weren't coming. But why in mourning, dear ? I thought you had left it off. Not another loss, I hope ?

[MRS. SHARPE *has risen and rung the bell.*]

MRS. TOMPKINS

Not your cousin, the baronet ?

MRS. DE HOOLEY

[*Seating herself.*] Her late Majesty, the Queen of Naples.

MISS KITE

[*She winks at the others.*] Must be very expensive, belonging to Court circles. Don't you find it so ?

MRS. DE HOOLEY

My dear, you can have no conception. There are times, I assure you, when I wish I had been born one of the people.

[*A German band out in the Square begins to play. The sound comes muffled.*]

MRS. TOMPKINS

Hark !

MISS KITE

Shall I open the window a little way, dear! The fog has lifted. We shall be able to hear better. [*She half rises.*]

[STASIA *has entered with a jug of hot water.*]

MRS. SHARPE

No, dear. If they see a lady, they'll expect something. Stasia, you just open the window a little way.

STASIA

Gar on. Why not pay up yer tuppence and enjoy the luxury of feeling honest? Only a 'a'penny a-piece.

MRS. SHARPE

You do as you are told.

STASIA

[*She goes to the window and throws it open. Calls out.*] Pl'y up. We're all a-listening!

MRS. SHARPE

You baggage!

[STASIA *goes out laughing.*]

MRS. TOMPKINS

I wonder at your keeping that girl.

MISS KITE

You got her from Walworth Jail, didn't you, dear?

MRS. SHARPE

Industrial school.

MISS KITE

My mistake, dear. I was speaking to one of the matrons about her only the other day. Very bad stock. The mother—well, we needn't go into particulars. [*Giggles.*] Hope you're getting her cheap, dear.

MRS. SHARPE

If she can do any better for herself, the door's open. And if it comes to talk about getting things cheap—especially candles——

MRS. TOMPKINS

She's not the class of girl to have about the place. I've always said so.

MRS. DE HOOLEY

It does seem to me that when you are catering for ladies and gentlemen——

MISS KITE

And when one remembers there are young girls about the house. [*To* MRS. TOMPKINS] Is it true, dear, that dear Miss Tompkins is engaged to Mr. Wright? Can we congratulate you?

MRS. TOMPKINS

Well, nothing is absolutely *settled.*

MISS KITE

Oh! Oh, I do hope she gets him. Because she has worked hard, poor girl.

MRS. TOMPKINS

Yes, and if paint and powder could have done it——

[*The* COLLECTOR *for the German band appears at the window. He thrusts his little bag on the end of a stick through the opening.*]

COLLECTOR

For ze moosik—you vill gif someting? Yes?

MRS. SHARPE

Go away. We don't give to beggars.

COLLECTOR

For ze moosik—yes ?

MISS KITE

The persistence of the man !

MRS. SHARPE

We never encourage foreigners.

COLLECTOR

Yes ?

MRS. SHARPE

No. I shall call the police—polizei !

COLLECTOR

Pigs !

MRS. SHARPE

[*Who has risen and crossed, bangs the window.*]

MISS KITE

Did you hear that ? Called us pigs !

MRS. DE HOOLEY

It's surprising how well they know English.

MRS. SHARPE

[*Reseating herself.*] You'll take another cup of tea ?

MRS. TOMPKINS

[*She has risen. She is still ruffled from her encounter with* MISS KITE.] Thank you, Mrs. Sharpe, but there are one or two little things I have to see to.

MISS KITE

I hope you don't mind what I said just now about dear Vivian. Only my little joke.

MRS. TOMPKINS

Of course, if it was only a joke——

MRS. SHARPE

You're sure you won't have another cup ?

MRS. TOMPKINS

Quite, thank you, dear. To tell you the truth, I rather want to be upstairs when my old man comes in. There's a little dressing-down I owe him that he got out of last night. [*She laughs.*]

MISS KITE

[*Laughs also.*] He doesn't often dodge it, does he, dear ? Not when you're feeling yourself.

MRS. TOMPKINS

Well, I flatter myself he knows what I think of him. [*Laughing, goes out, well pleased with herself.*]

MRS. DE HOOLEY

Really, I feel quite sorry for that poor man. Of course he *is* a beast.

MISS KITE

My dear, he can give her as good as he gets.

MRS. SHARPE

How they keep it up is a mystery to me. It's cat and dog from the time they get up in the morning till they go to bed at night.

MRS. DE HOOLEY

Young Larkcom calls them "Darby and Joan."

[*They all laugh.*]

MISS KITE

She didn't like what I said about the girl. [*Giggles.*] And it's only the truth. The shameless way she has set her cap at that poor man! Makes one blush for one's sex.

MRS. DE HOOLEY

Merely a common racing man, wasn't he ?

MRS. SHARPE

A bookmaker—until he lost his voice.

MISS KITE

They say it was the funniest thing at the end: to hear him trying to shout [*Mimics*] "Two to one, bar one." Nobody could hear him a yard away.

MRS. DE HOOLEY

You think he's really as rich as he makes out he is ?

MRS. SHARPE

Well, I wouldn't like to say that—of anybody.

MISS KITE

Well, my advice to her would be to marry him quickly and take him away—somewhere where our Israelitish friend Jape Samuels won't be able to get hold of him—unless, of course, she loves him for himself alone.

MRS. SHARPE

I've noticed Samuels has been pretty soapy to him of late. What is the little try-on? Have you heard anything?

MISS KITE

A little, my dear. [*She winks.*] Can't very well help it if people will talk loud enough to be heard the other side of a deal door. Of course, he may have a silver-mine to sell, and it may be worth all that he says it is, and then, again, it mayn't.

[*The clock strikes the half-hour—two strokes.*]

MRS. SHARPE

Half-past. [*Rising.*] I must be seeing about dinner. It's a funny world. [*To* MRS. DE HOOLEY] Won't you take anything more?

MRS. DE HOOLEY

Nothing more, thank you.

MISS KITE

Funny people in it.

MRS. SHARPE

[*Has suggested to her another slice of cake.*]

MISS KITE

No, thanks, dear. What is the menu to-night?

MRS. SHARPE

[*She is by the sideboard.*] Well, I thought a curry would be a pleasant change this evening.

MISS KITE

Ah yes, just the day for it. And your curries, dear, are always so good.

MRS. SHARPE

Oh, I'm so glad you like them. You're sure you've finished?

MISS KITE

Quite, dear, thank you.

MRS. SHARPE

I'll send the girl to clear away.

[MRS. SHARPE, *unobserved, has locked the tantalus. She goes out through the folding-doors.*]

MISS KITE

[*Looks round the room and sees that* MRS. SHARPE *has gone.*] That means that the veal is a bit "off." Such a useful thing, a little curry powder, for disguising the smell.

MRS. DE HOOLEY

[*She sighs.*] I suppose they are all alike—lodging-house keepers.

MISS KITE

Cats, my dear, all of them. There's no other word for them—cats.

MRS. DE HOOLEY

[*As together they go towards the door.*] It's a wicked world.

MISS KITE

Ah, you may well say that. And it don't get any better, that's the sad——

[MRS. DE HOOLEY *has opened the door. The beam of sunlight falls full upon their faces, making them both blink for the moment.*]

MRS. DE HOOLEY

Well, I never ! Quite a treat to see the sun.

MISS KITE

Well, myself, I don't care for it.

MRS. DE HOOLEY

You don't !

MISS KITE

My dear, it shows us all up too much. [*She giggles ; and they go out, leaving the door open.*]

The stage remains empty for a few seconds. Then the front door is opened with a latch-key. MAJOR TOMPKINS *enters. He is a fine, well-set-up man, with a military bearing ; a ruddy face with white hair and moustache. He wears a frock coat, tightly buttoned, silk hat, and a single eye-glass. He carries gloves and a walking-stick. He looks into the room, and his eyes fasten on the remains of the tea. He looks out and up and down the stairs and passage ; then enters the room, humming an air. Hurriedly he empties the remainder of the biscuits, together with the cake, into his hat. This done, still humming and with a jaunty step, he makes for the door. But as he reaches it :*

There re-enters MRS. SHARPE.]

MAJOR

Ah, Mrs. Sharpe, good afternoon. And how is Mrs. Sharpe this afternoon ?

MRS. SHARPE

Quite well, thank you, Major Tompkins.

MAJOR

Delighted !—delighted !

MRS. SHARPE

[*She glances at the table, and takes in the facts. She closes the door with a click, and stands in front of it. She makes a quick movement to try to see into the hat. By exceeding nimbleness he frustrates her.*] Won't you put your hat down, Major ?

MAJOR

I thank you, Mrs. Sharpe, but I'm rather in a hurry.

MRS. SHARPE

[*With sudden fierceness.*] And so am I—for

thirty-six pounds eighteen shillings and fourpence. Which unless you pay me by twelve o'clock to-morrow I intend to sue you for in the County Court. And that before we are either of us a week older.

MAJOR

Let us be business-like.

MRS. SHARPE

Most happy.

MAJOR

You can sue me, Mrs. Sharpe, and you won't get so much as a damned penny.

MRS. SHARPE

Perhaps not ; perhaps yes.

MAJOR

I propose to you, Mrs. Sharpe, that you accept my bill for one hundred pounds at three months. By which date the chances are that my daughter will be Mrs. Joseph Wright, and that I shall be in a position to meet it.

MRS. SHARPE

And meanwhile I am to go on keeping you all three.

3

MAJOR

[*Shrugs his shoulders.*] I put it to you as a gamble. [*Close to her—confidential.*] Mr. Wright has made my daughter a formal offer of marriage. Vivian hesitates a little. It is natural. But she has sense. She will listen to her old father's advice, [*with a chuckle*] especially seeing it will be to her own advantage.

MRS. SHARPE

Hardly to her advantage paying your debts.

MAJOR

[*He seats himself at the table.*] Hardly to her advantage allowing it to appear in all the papers that her father is being sued for board and lodging. Family pride, Mrs. Sharpe—there is such a thing as family pride.

MRS. SHARPE

[*Yielding.*] Well, only mind——

MAJOR

[*He has taken out his pocket-book and his pen.*] A business man, Mrs. Sharpe, is always prepared for business. Let me see, to-day is—— [*He is filling in the bill.*]

[VIVIAN *has entered unobserved. She is in walking-dress. She is a tall, handsome girl, dark, with strong but finely cut features ; dark, passionate eyes ; and bears towards all things a weary, mocking manner.*]

VIVIAN

[*She looks from one to the other ; closes door.*] And if I don't ?

MAJOR

My dear !

VIVIAN

Oh, let us talk plainly. [*She crosses, taking off her hat, etc.*] You are persuading Mrs. Sharpe to bet on the chance of my accepting Mr. Joseph Wright's clammy and, generally speaking, not over-clean hand.

MRS. SHARPE

Well, to be candid, Miss Tompkins, I don't see any other hope myself of my ever getting my money.

MAJOR

And to be equally candid with everybody, nor more do I.

VIVIAN

I should risk it, Mrs. Sharpe. I think you will win.

MAJOR

Mrs. Sharpe, you hear. You——

VIVIAN

Of course, there *is* the possibility that in some moment of self-respect I may be tempted to tell him how the mere touch of him is loathsome to me.

MAJOR

Vivian! My dear!

VIVIAN

I merely mention it that everything may be quite fair. Mrs. Sharpe will judge for herself whether in the end I am more likely to be influenced by self-respect or self-interest.

MAJOR

[*Whispers.*] A little fretful. But plenty of sense.

MRS. SHARPE

[*She has decided to chance it.*] Mind, if it isn't met——

MAJOR

It shall be met, Mrs. Sharpe, on the honour of a soldier.

MRS. SHARPE

[*Putting the bill in her pocket.*] I'm putting my trust more in *Miss* Vivian.

[*She goes out.*]

MAJOR

[*He answers her with a pleasant laugh and a wave of the hand. Then he turns to his daughter.*] My dear child, I cannot tell you—— [*She is carrying his hat towards the window.*] What are you doing? Vivian! [*She opens the window and flings the contents of the hat into the street.*] How dare you! Damn your infernal impudence! How dare you! [*Having closed the window, she faces him. The bluster falls from him.*] The wastefulness—the wicked wastefulness! [*She hands him the empty hat.*] Robbing your own father to fling it to the mere street brats! Look at 'em!—look at 'em! [*She hands him his stick and gloves. Again he collapses, and taking them, goes towards the door.*] My one weakness: a nibble of something sweet with the last glass—just before going to bed. [*From tears again to fury.*] And you knew it, you——

[MRS. TOMPKINS *has entered with a soft step and smiling face. A silence.*]

MRS. TOMPKINS

I *thought* I heard your voice.

MAJOR

[*Snarls.*] Ah, you did, did you? Yes, some of us *have* got long ears.

MRS. TOMPKINS

One doesn't want them particularly long to hear you, when you are bullying a woman!

MAJOR

Bullying! I? Why haven't you brought up your daughter to respect her father?

MRS. TOMPKINS

Vivian, haven't I always impressed it upon you

that it is your duty to hide the contempt you can't help feeling for your father?

MAJOR

[*Snarls.*] Ah! look at her, standing there grinning—after all that I've done for her.

MRS. TOMPKINS

That *you*——

MAJOR

Wasn't it I who brought old Wright here? Haven't I invited him to my own club—and been asked to resign myself in consequence? Don't I listen to his damned silly stories?

MRS. TOMPKINS

And borrow half-crowns from him.

MAJOR

It all helps. It makes him feel one of the family.

MRS. TOMPKINS

The family don't get many of them.

MAJOR

Don't! Who keeps both of you—in luxury?

MRS. TOMPKINS

Mrs. Sharpe!

MAJOR

Mrs. Sharpe! You throw that in my teeth, you; when your own father died bankrupt.

MRS. TOMPKINS

Why did you swindle him?

MAJOR

Who swindled him?

MRS. TOMPKINS

You! Didn't you take all my money?

MAJOR

Your money! Who cheated——

MRS. TOMPKINS

Who stole——

MAJOR

Who——

[JOEY WRIGHT *has entered, a man of a little over 60 perhaps, with the face and figure of Silenus: a leering, blear-eyed, perspiring person. He speaks always in a hoarse whisper; wears extravagant clothes and a quantity of jewellery.*]

[*In a moment the* MAJOR *and* MRS. TOMPKINS *are all smiles and smirks.*]

MAJOR

Ah! and how is——

MRS. TOMPKINS

Good after——

WRIGHT

[*He waves them aside.*] Finish it out—finish it out. Don't let me spoil sport. Only looked in to ask Miss Vivian if she wouldn't come to the theatre with me this evening. Got a box for the Gaiety. [*He goes to her; she moves a step away.*]

MAJOR

Delighted, I'm sure. [*He is making frantic signs to Vivian.*] The dear child will be delighted.

MRS. TOMPKINS

You'll be able to wear your new frock, dear.

VIVIAN

Thanks. I'm not feeling particularly inclined for the theatre to-night.

MAJOR

Not even with the little supper—the little supper afterwards at the Savoy? [*He is winking at* JOEY WRIGHT.]

WRIGHT

You might come. You never will. Shall begin to think you don't like me.

VIVIAN

[*Turns and looks at him, and as she turns away again she hesitates.*] I'll think it over.

WRIGHT

[*He looks round at the parents questioningly.*]

MRS. TOMPKINS

[*Whispers to him.*] That'll be all right.

MAJOR

You have the cab ready waiting at the door.

WRIGHT

[*He nods his understanding.*] That's all I came for. Sorry to have interrupted. [*He goes out.*]

[*The* MAJOR *carefully closes the door.* VIVIAN *has taken up her hat.*]

MAJOR

Well, what are you going to do?

VIVIAN

"Think it over"—for myself and by myself. [*Her eyes are blazing.*]

[*A silence.*]

MAJOR

[*Looks at* VIVIAN, *then at his wife.*]

MRS. TOMPKINS

[*They speak in low tones.*] Perhaps we shall only irritate her.

MAJOR

Plain enough where she gets her damned obstinacy from. [*He flings out of the room.*]

MRS. TOMPKINS

[*Following. The quarrel continues up the stairs.*] Yes. I'd be sorry to think that she took after you. Eh, what do you say?

[VIVIAN *crosses, carrying her hat and cloak. The shaft of sunlight has grown stronger. Catching her eyes, it causes her to pause. She stands a moment looking at it. A faint smile comes. She then lays down what she is carrying, and stretching out her hands, warms them childishly in the light. Thus she is standing, her face uplifted to the light, when* CHRISTOPHER *enters.*

[CHRISTOPHER *takes her outstretched hands, and in silence they stand just within the doorway, illumined by the sun. After a while he releases her hands and closes the door. The room darkens. She lets her hands fall by her side, and moves away.*]

CHRISTOPHER

I crossed the old folks on the stairs. [*Laughs.*] I thought you might be here.

VIVIAN

I was just going up to dress.

CHRISTOPHER

There's no hurry, is there?

VIVIAN

Yes.

CHRISTOPHER

Why?

VIVIAN

My future husband may be coming back.

[*A silence.*]

CHRISTOPHER

You have made up your mind ?

VIVIAN

[*She nods.*] What else is to be done ?

CHRISTOPHER

Vivian, listen. Artists do make money—heaps of money.

VIVIAN

After how many years ? We would both be old.

CHRISTOPHER

[*An evil look in his face.*] There are pictures people *will* buy and pay well for. I can knock them off quickly. They don't want Art.

VIVIAN

Ah ! don't. It was why I loved you. You seemed to me the only human creature with a soul I'd ever met. Let me respect you.

CHRISTOPHER

I don't want your respect. I want you. [*He seizes her. The passion is in his eyes.*]

VIVIAN

Hark! Go!

CHRISTOPHER

Vivian! You must—you shall.

VIVIAN

Don't be a fool. [*She frees herself from him.*] Do you want to sink to my level?

CHRISTOPHER

Yes. I tell you I want you. I——

[*There enters* HARRY LARKCOM, *about five-and-twenty, a cheerful young bounder, loudly dressed. He carries about him the atmosphere of the music-hall. With him* JAPE SAMUELS, *an older man, a Jew of the most objectionable type, now oily, now aggressive. His dress is that of the city man.* VIVIAN *collects her belongings and moves to go out.* LARKCOM, *the low comedian of the house, opens the door for her, bowing with hand on heart.* SAMUELS *kisses his hand after her. She goes out.* LARKCOM *closes the door, and they both turn round with a laugh.* CHRISTOPHER *has noticed, bit his lip, and turned away.*]

SAMUELS

How are you getting on?

CHRISTOPHER

I *have* begun them. You shall have them by the end of next week.

SAMUELS

Good man. Get you another job when they're done. Keep them thpithy. You know what I mean: don't watht too much paint on the clothe. [*Laughs.*]

CHRISTOPHER

I quite understand. Thank you—very much. [*He goes out.*]

SAMUELS

Don't mention it. [*He kicks the door to after him. Turns to* LARKCOM.] Keep him up to it. I can thell ath many ath he can paint of the thort at twithe what I pay him. Tell you what I want you to do for me.

LARKCOM

[*He is unlocking the tantalus, with a key from his own pocket.*] Found it out by accident. Fits it like a glove. [*They laugh.*] See that the old girl ain't coming.

SAMUELS

[*He peeps out, closes the door again.*] It'th all right. I want you to take old Wright out to lunth next Wednethday at Romanoth. [*He thrusts his face forward with his finger at the side of his nose.*] And don't be thingy with the drinkth.

LARKCOM

[*Laughs.*]

SAMUELS

Put him in a cab afterwardth and bring him up to my little plathe in the thity. We'll have everything jutht ready for him to thign.

LARKCOM

You don't think he's a bit too fly ?

SAMUELS

[*The finger to the nose again.*] Have a girl with you.

LARKCOM

You are a rare old gimlet, you are. [*Has prepared what he thinks to be two whiskies-and-water. He hands one to* SAMUELS.]

SAMUELS

Got to be up to a trick or two in thith world if you don't want to be left. [*They have clicked glasses. They now take their first pull.*] What ith it ?

[*They look at one another with wry faces.*]

LARKCOM

Some muck she's got for palming off upon old Joey when he's drunk.

SAMUELS

Old thief !

LARKCOM

Makes you lose your faith in human nature,

don't it ? [*He crams the half-empty tumblers into the sideboard.*]

[STASIA *has entered from the other room. Her business for the next few minutes is clearing the tea-table.*]

Hello, what price the belle of Bloomsbury ! [*He makes to embrace her. She slaps his face.*] All right. Now you don't have what I was going to give you.

STASIA

That'll save trouble all round.

SAMUELS

[*Laughs.*]

LARKCOM

Save you the trouble of living up to them. [*Produces from his pocket a box, opens it, and displays a pair of cheap, gaudy earrings.*] Emeralds.

STASIA

Real old bottle glass.

LARKCOM

[*He appeals to Samuels.*] Ain't they real emeralds ?

SAMUELS

[*Examines them, with the air of an expert.*] Fourteen carat. Thall be upthairth if you want me. [*He goes out.*]

LARKCOM

[*He thrusts the earrings again under her nose.*] Knock at my door, softly, about ten o'clock to-night, if you feel you want 'em. [*Snaps the case. Winks. Goes out.*]

[STASIA *goes into the other room; is heard laying the table.*]

[*Enter* MRS. SHARPE. *She goes to the sideboard. Her business is the taking of wine-glasses and arranging them on a tray. The folding doors are partly open.*]

MRS. SHARPE

[*Her back is to the dining-room. She holds up one by one the glasses to the light; polishes them when need be with her pocket-handkerchief.*] Is that you, Stasia?

STASIA

That's me.

MRS. SHARPE

What are you doing ?

STASIA

Lying the table for dinner.

MRS. SHARPE

Have you taken up everybody their hot water ?

STASIA

Yus. I've taken them up their 'ot water—all the rotten lot of them.

MRS. SHARPE

What do you mean ?—" All the rotten lot of them " ?

STASIA

Well, so they are. Young Christopher Penny ! I did think 'e was a cut above the others.

MRS. SHARPE

Umph ! What's *he* doing ?

STASIA

Painting pictures. Got an order for a dozen. I told 'im straight. " You tike care the police don't see 'em," I says, "if the others are going to be like that."

MRS. SHARPE

[*With the snort that does duty for her laugh.*] As bad as all that?

STASIA

Somebody's put 'im up to it. Old Wright, I shouldn't wonder—old beast!

MRS. SHARPE

That'll do—that'll do. Don't you be so free with your tongue.

STASIA

Well, so 'e is; wanting to marry a girl young enough to be his daughter. She's no better. She's going to sell 'erself all right enough.

MRS. SHARPE

How do you know?

STASIA

Just called me in to help 'er on with 'er new frock. You know: the one without any neck and arms. She's going out to the theatre with 'im.

MRS. SHARPE

Glad to hear it.

STASIA

Ah! they're a rotten lot, all of them. There's old "Darby and Joan" been jawing at each other ever since 'e come in, calling each other every name under the sun. Then there's Jew-boy Samuels planning it with young Larkcom 'ow to swindle everybody. Didn't know I was in the next room a-listening. D'ye 'ear old Kite slanging me just now?

MRS. SHARPE

Yes. What was it about?

STASIA

Oh! 'cos I went in without knocking—caught 'er with the paint-pot in 'er 'and. Old 'Ooley's another of 'em, makes me sick—practising court curtseys in front of the looking-glass all to 'erself—old fool! Got those glasses ready?

MRS. SHARPE

Yes, they're ready.

STASIA

[*Entering.*] We're no better, you know, you and me. You're an old thief.

MRS. SHARPE

[*Speechless.*] A thief! What do you——

STASIA

So you are. So am I—and wuss. What's the good of us all, that's what I want to know? What's the good of us?

MRS. SHARPE

[*Repeating helplessly.*] What's the good of us?

STASIA

[*She has put down the tray again which she at first had taken up. She comes down and faces* MRS. SHARPE.] What's the use of us? What's the good of us to ourselves or to anybody else? What——

[*There comes a knock at the street door—one single, clear, distinctive knock. It sounds mysteriously, coming so unexpectedly into the darkening room.* MRS. SHARPE *and* STASIA *both start, and stand a moment looking at one another.*]

MRS. SHARPE

What was that ?

STASIA

Somebody knocking at the door.

MRS. SHARPE

Who can it be ?

[*The knock is repeated.*]

It must be some beggar.

STASIA

P'raps it's a visitor.

MRS. SHARPE

A visitor ? What sort of visitor would——

[*The knock is again repeated.*]

STASIA

Seems determined to come in.

MRS. SHARPE

Go and see who it is.

[STASIA *goes out, closing the door behind her.*]

[MRS. SHARPE, *puzzled at the passing of the time, goes to the keyhole ; peeps through ; returns to her glasses; goes to the keyhole again—listens; the handle turns.* MRS. SHARPE *darts away just in time.*

[STASIA *re-enters. She closes the door and stands smiling—at nothing in particular.*]

MRS. SHARPE

Well? What are you grinning at?

STASIA

Nothin'. [*But still she stands smiling.*]

MRS. SHARPE

What's the matter with you? Who is it?

STASIA

'E's come about the room.

MRS. SHARPE

The room! What—Did you put up that card, in spite of my telling you not to?

STASIA

Yus.

MRS. SHARPE

[*A movement of impatience.*] What's he like?

STASIA

'E ain't the usual sort.

MRS. SHARPE

Thank God for that. Is he a gentleman ?

STASIA

[*She seems to be in a dream.*] I dunno.

MRS. SHARPE

[*Again a movement of impatience.*] Young or old ?

STASIA

[*Still with the same exasperating, dreamy smile.*] I dunno.

MRS. SHARPE

Ah, you fool ! Show him in. [*She arranges her cuffs, straightens her cap.*]

STASIA

[*Opens the door.*] Come in.

[*The* STRANGER *enters ; a slightly stooping figure, clothes—if one look at them closely—somewhat shabby, the long coat somewhat old-fashioned. His hat, his staff, quaintly suggestive of the days of pilgrimage. What age he might be it would be difficult to say; there are moments when the deep eyes would seem to speak of many sorrows. But more often—and always when he smiles—it is a face radiant with youth. In some mysterious way he brings into the room with him an atmosphere of dignity. Yet there is nothing "important" about the* STRANGER. *If there be anything great about him, it lies in his simplicity, his gentleness. He bows to* MRS. SHARPE. *It is the simplest of courtesies, yet one fails to see how it could express more were she the daughter of a hundred earls. And* MRS. SHARPE, *returning the bow, becomes, for the moment, a lady.*]

THE STRANGER

Good afternoon.

MRS. SHARPE

Good afternoon. You have called about a room? [*She has clothed herself in her most ladylike tones and manners.*]

THE STRANGER

Your little maid tells me there is one vacant.

MRS. SHARPE

Yes. There does happen to be just one. You can go, Stasia.

[STASIA *goes to take up her tray—the* STRANGER *interposes.*]

THE STRANGER

[*To* MRS. SHARPE.] May I ? It is so heavy.

[*He carries out the tray.* STASIA *stares after him open-mouthed. Then at* MRS. SHARPE, *who is also staring.*]

THE STRANGER

[*Returning—to* STASIA.] I have placed it on the table. Was that right ?

MRS. SHARPE

Quite right. [*To* STASIA, *who is on her way out.*] Shut the door after you.

[STASIA, *as in a dream, goes out. Closes the door.*]

Won't you be seated ?

THE STRANGER

Thank you. [*One of the easy-chairs stands by*

the table. He pushes it nearer the fire.] Will you take this chair ?

MRS. SHARPE

[*Who is not used to having chairs offered her, accepts it somewhat awkwardly.*] Thank you. [*She sits stiffly.*]

[*The* STRANGER *crosses, seats himself the other side of the fire. The twilight is deepening. The red glow from the fire illumines their faces.*]

THE STRANGER

[*Smiling.*] Now we can talk business.

MRS. SHARPE

[*She bows. To bow frequently and very stiffly is one of her ideas of high-class manners.*] To begin with—you will excuse the question, I'm sure—but [*she is eyeing critically his clothes*] what are you ?

THE STRANGER

I—am a wanderer.

MRS. SHARPE

You mean a traveller ?

THE STRANGER

[*Accepts the correction.*] A traveller.

MRS. SHARPE

For pleasure?

THE STRANGER

For pleasure.

MRS. SHARPE

[*She looks at him again; it is a puzzling problem.*] You see, I have to be perhaps a little particular. My clientèle is drawn, as a rule, from the higher middle-classes. [*The* STRANGER *gives his grave attention.*] At the present moment I have staying with me the cousin to a baronet. Representing capital, we have Mr. Samuels, the great silver-mine proprietor. We have also a retired Major and family—highly connected. Mr. Penny, the eminent artist—you may have heard of him—

THE STRANGER

I live so out of the world.

MRS. SHARPE

—Has his studio at the top of the house. My

first floor is occupied by an exceedingly wealthy man—for years a prominent figure in the sporting world. Indeed, I may say that *all* our little circle are persons of more or less distinction.

THE STRANGER

It will be a privilege to meet them.

MRS. SHARPE

[*She flashes a suspicious glance, but encounters only his eyes of grave sincerity.*] My charges, as you will understand, are of necessity a little more than those of the common boarding-house.

THE STRANGER

That is only to be expected.

MRS. SHARPE

[*Bows.*] For the room I have to offer you: a charming apartment on the—just above the second floor; together with full board, consisting of——

THE STRANGER

[*He smiles away the details.*] Of everything that is needful. It goes without saying.

MRS. SHARPE

[*Bows again.*] I usually ask two pounds ten a week. [*He may be about to speak ; she waves him back into patience.*] To *you*, seeing you—[*she cannot think of any other reason*]—are a traveller—[*with a burst of generosity*]—we'll say two pounds.

THE STRANGER

But is that quite fair ?

MRS. SHARPE

[*Ready for battle.*] Fair !

THE STRANGER

To you. I am not a rich man—as you, with your quick woman's sympathy, have divined. But I have sufficient. I can afford to pay you your proper price.

MRS. SHARPE

The two pounds will be quite satisfactory.

THE STRANGER

You are sure ?

MRS. SHARPE

Quite sure.

THE STRANGER

It is very kind of you—very kind indeed.

MRS. SHARPE

[*Again the bow.*] Gas, of course, will be an extra.

THE STRANGER

Of course.

MRS. SHARPE

Coals——

THE STRANGER

[*Again he smiles away her details.*] We shall not quarrel. You have been so very considerate as it is, I feel I can leave myself entirely in your hands.

MRS. SHARPE

Well, I always try to be fair, and—— [*She looks up and meets his gaze full upon her; an embarrassed silence falls upon her.*] Do you ever get taken in—cheated?

THE STRANGER

[*Smiling.*] Sometimes—by cheats.

[*A silence.*]

MRS. SHARPE

How do you know I'm not one?

THE STRANGER

We old travellers—it is a conceit of ours that we can tell ladies and gentlemen from cheats.

MRS. SHARPE

You think a lodging-house keeper can be a lady?

THE STRANGER

Why not?

MRS. SHARPE

No, I suppose there's no reason. In my own case, as it happens, I really am a lady.

THE STRANGER

You see, I was right.

MRS. SHARPE

My late husband was a solicitor. I used to have my At Homes in this very room—on third Fridays.

THE STRANGER

And it is the third Friday of the month to-day.

MRS. SHARPE

Why, so it is. I had forgotten. [*Remembering, becomes the landlady again.*] Would you like to go up to your room now ? We dine at six-thirty. [*She rises.*]

THE STRANGER

[*Rising.*] Thank you. That will just give me time.

MRS. SHARPE

I'll just see first that everything—— [*He has taken up his hat and stick, and is moving towards the door. She pauses.*] Did I say two pounds a week ? [*Something is worrying her ; it causes her to speak in an angry, aggressive tone.*]

THE STRANGER

It should have been two pounds ten. You were kind enough to reduce it——

MRS. SHARPE

I must have been thinking of some other room. It should have been one pound ten.

THE STRANGER

[*Stops.*] Then I decline to take it. The two pounds I can well afford.

MRS. SHARPE

One pound ten are my terms. If you are bent on paying more, you can go elsewhere. You'll find plenty to oblige you.

THE STRANGER

[*He looks at her.*] Women are so wilful. [*Smiling*] And you kind women are the worst of all. [*He has taken her hand. She laughs.*]

[*They go out.*]

[STASIA *enters by the folding doors. She goes to sideboard; takes from a drawer some napkins; brings them to the table. She forgets them, stands idly by the table gazing out of the window.* MRS. SHARPE *re-enters.* STASIA, *dreaming, neither sees nor hears her.* MRS. SHARPE *stands for awhile looking at her. A new look has come into* MRS. SHARPE'S *face, a new note in her voice, a new spirit has stolen into the house.*]

MRS. SHARPE

What are you looking at?

STASIA

[*She wakes with a start.*] Nothin'. [*Begins folding the napkins.*]

MRS. SHARPE

[*She comes nearer; looks again at the little pale face.*] Like to put on your hat—get a breath of fresh air before dinner?

STASIA

[*Stares.*] D'ye mean it?

MRS. SHARPE

[*Takes the napkins quietly from her.*] I'll finish laying the table. Don't be too long.

STASIA

[*She is off; half-way to the door something suddenly stops her.*] Sure you can spare me?

MRS. SHARPE

That'll be all right.

STASIA

I won't be long. [*She runs swiftly out.*]

MRS. SHARPE

[*She goes on folding up the napkins. Then she, too, forgets them. They fall from her hand. A smile gradually breaks over the old face, strangely altering it; she, too, seems to be falling into a way *of dreaming.* "And you kind women are the worst of all." [*She whispers the words, the while her uplifted face becomes transformed with a great tenderness as towards all things.*]

THE CURTAIN FALLS

CHARACTERS IN THE PLAY

Joey Wright	A Retired Bookmaker.
Christopher Penny . . .	A Painter.
Major Tompkins . . .	Retired.
Mrs. Tompkins . . .	His Wife.
Vivian	His Daughter.
Jape Samuels	Of the City.
Harry Larkcom . . .	His Jackal.
Miss Kite	Unattached.
Mrs. Percival de Hooley . .	Cousin to Sir George Tweedle, Bart.
Stasia	The Slavey.
Mrs. Sharpe	The Landlady.
The Third Floor Back.	

THE PLAY

SCENE

The same. It is dark. A faint glow from the fire intensifies the shadows. The light from the dining-room outlines the folding doors. The light from the street lamps without struggles faint and mysterious through the windows. The two easy-chairs have been placed one each side of the fire.

[STASIA *enters; leaves the door open behind her. The light from the passage lifts a little the darkness of the room. She strikes a match, climbs upon a chair and lights the three branches of the gaselier. And the room takes three strides into feeble light. An improvement has taken place in* STASIA'S *appearance. Her hair is tidier, her face and hands cleaner.*]

[*A sound as of a sudden burst of talking after a silence is heard from the next room.* STASIA *stands a moment listening; it dies. She crosses to the windows, pulls down the blinds, arranges the curtains.*]

[VIVIAN *comes in. She is in evening dress, somewhat décolleté.*]

VIVIAN

Haven't they finished dinner yet?

STASIA

[*She goes to the folding doors and peeps through the keyhole.*] They're a-toying with the dessert. Why didn't you come down? Off your feed? [*Her voice has changed—has taken to itself a childish note.*]

VIVIAN

[*Who has seated herself in one of the easy-chairs.*] I had a headache. [*She has taken an illustrated paper from the table.*]

STASIA

Going out to the theatre, ain't you?

VIVIAN

Yes.

STASIA

With the old 'un ?

VIVIAN

Will you kindly mind your own business ?

STASIA

Suppose I oughtn't to blime you. [*She speaks more to herself than to* VIVIAN, *who, glancing through her paper, appears to take no notice.*] We've all of us got to live—somehow. [*Aloud*] You ain't seen the new lodger ?

VIVIAN

Oh ! Is there a new lodger ?

STASIA

Came this evening, just before dinner. [*There is something in* STASIA'S *voice which causes* VIVIAN *to glance round at her.*]

VIVIAN

[*She turns again to her paper.*] What's he like ?

STASIA

[*She comes to* VIVIAN.] This ain't all the world, is it ?

VIVIAN

[*Looking up.*] What *do* you mean ?

STASIA

Us sort. [*With a gesture.*] All a-lyin' and a-cheatin' and a-snarlin'—despisin' one another—and ourselves. Ain't there anything else ?

[*A silence.*]

VIVIAN

Yes. There are sweet thoughts. And fine feelings. And self-respect. [*She turns to* STASIA.] But such things, Stasia, are only for rich folk.

STASIA

[*She goes slowly towards the door.*] Bit 'ard on us poor. [*Goes out.*]

[VIVIAN *drops her paper ; sits staring into the fire a few moments. The folding doors open, letting in the sound from the dining-room.* MRS. MAJOR TOMPKINS *enters and closes the door behind her. She is dressed quietly and effectively. With her entrance the atmosphere changes.*]

MRS. TOMPKINS

How's your headache ?

VIVIAN

I think it will be all right.

MRS. TOMPKINS

You didn't miss much. I *could* have eaten an artichoke. Of course your father grabs the dish and clears the lot. You know, you can afford to show a bit more shoulder. [*She goes to re-arrange the girl's dress.*]

VIVIAN

[*Shrinking away.*] Don't, please. I hate being mauled.

MRS. TOMPKINS

Funny girl you are! If you can't bear your own mother——

VIVIAN

It's only this evening. I'm feeling irritable. [*Her eyes still on the paper.*] What's the new lodger like?

MRS. TOMPKINS

Don't like him.

VIVIAN

Why not?

MRS. TOMPKINS

I can't explain it. He makes you feel uncomfortable. [*Resentfully*] His mere presence in the room—— [*She is at table choosing a paper, her back to the dining-room.*]

[*The folding doors have opened.* MISS KITE, *followed by* MRS. DE HOOLEY, *is entering :* MISS KITE *in what she herself would call a " killing " costume ;* MRS. DE HOOLEY *in " semi "-toilette.*]

VIVIAN

Quick !—quick !

[MRS. TOMPKINS *understands, but reaches the only remaining easy-chair a second behind the* KITE *woman, who slips down into it triumphant.* MRS. TOMPKINS, *giving her a " look," passes on with ostentatious indifference, and seats herself near the table.*]

MRS. DE HOOLEY

[*Taking a chair by* VIVIAN.] So sorry to hear of your headache.

VIVIAN

It's better now.

MRS. DE HOOLEY

So glad. You haven't seen our new guest?

VIVIAN

I have been hearing about him.

MRS. DE HOOLEY

He reminds me so of somebody I've met somewhere. [*She thinks a moment.*] Long ago.

MISS KITE

Well, so far as I can understand, she picked him up out of the street: not even a reference.

MRS. TOMPKINS

Do you mean that she has dared to introduce among ladies and gentlemen——

MISS KITE

My dear, a mere passer-by.

MRS. TOMPKINS

I *thought* there was something very wrong about him.

MISS KITE

We don't know *who* he may be.

JAPE SAMUELS *has entered from the dining-room*

closing the door behind him. He is smoking a fat cigar. He wears evening-dress—dinner-jacket—and one enormous diamond stud.]

MRS. TOMPKINS

[*To* JAPE.] What do *you* think of him?

SAMUELS

[*He is at table selecting a paper, his back to the others.*] Of the latetht addition to our little menadtherie? Well, to begin with, he'th not my idea of a thentleman.

MISS KITE

Looks to me as if he'd got money. [*She winks at* MRS. TOMPKINS, *who smiles back.*]

SAMUELS

[*Turns sharply.*] Why? What makth you think that?

MISS KITE

I don't know. He gives me that impression.

SAMUELS

Dethent enough thort of a chap, I darethay, in all other rethpecth. We can't help what we are born. [*He has the " Evening Standard " (white), " Globe " (pink), and " Westminster " (green) in his hand. He places them one inside the other, so that only the " Standard " shows. He sits near the table.*]

[*Then enter the* MAJOR *and* WRIGHT, *arm-in-arm, followed by* LARKCOM. WRIGHT *is in evening-dress, gorgeous with jewellery ; the* MAJOR *is also in evening-dress ;* LARKCOM *wears his check suit.* LARKCOM *closes the door and joins* SAMUELS. WRIGHT *and the* MAJOR *are laughing—the* MAJOR *boisterously,* WRIGHT *voicelessly.* WRIGHT *has been telling the* MAJOR *a smutty story.*]

MAJOR

Best story I've ever heard ! " She'd taken them with her." [*Laughs again and digs him in the ribs.*] I must remember that one.

VIVIAN

[*At entrance of her father she crosses to the desk, where she seats herself, her back to the room, and writes or pretends to write a letter.*]

[*The moment she vacates the chair,* MRS. DE HOOLEY *rises to take it, but* LARKCOM *darts across and flings himself into it just in front of her.*]

LARKCOM

Won by a neck. [*Laughs at her, settles himself, and takes out his pipe, which he fills and lights.*]

MRS. DE HOOLEY

[*She bestows disdain upon* LARKCOM ; *then goes to small work-table, fetches her work-basket and brings it to the table, where she sits within whispering distance of* MISS KITE.]

MAJOR

[*Crosses to table and turns over the papers.*] Anybody seen the "Globe"? [*To* SAMUELS] What paper have you got?

SAMUELS

[*Shows him the outside one.*] Thtandard.

MAJOR

Where the devil has the "Globe" got to? [*He goes on tour of discovery.*]

MRS. TOMPKINS

[*She touches* WRIGHT, *who has taken the chair vacated by* MRS. DE HOOLEY.] She'll be ready in a few minutes. What do you think of the new boarder?

WRIGHT

[*Shakes his head.*] Not my fancy.

LARKCOM

[*Turning to* WRIGHT.] He's got no conversation—not what *I* call conversation.

MAJOR

I found him a fool. [*He has rummaged among the music on the piano—glanced in passing at the desk.*]

MRS. TOMPKINS

[*With a laugh.*] Yes, I noticed you and he seemed to be getting on very well together.

[STASIA *has entered, more or less unnoticed. She brings the coffee in on tray.*]

STASIA

[*She stops first in front of* MRS. TOMPKINS.] Kaufee.

[MRS. TOMPKINS *takes a cup.*]

[*The* MAJOR *goes to table, snatches a paper and seats himself between the table and* MRS. DE HOOLEY. STASIA *goes her round with the coffee.*]

WRIGHT

[*To* MRS. TOMPKINS.] We don't want him here. Spoils the party.

LARKCOM

He's not our class.

MISS KITE

I can't make out whether he's a young man trying to look old, or an old man trying to look young.

MAJOR

I hate a man with eyes that you can't get away from.

MRS. DE HOOLEY

[*In her soft, slow voice, still dreaming.*] It was a long time ago.

MRS. TOMPKINS

We must make it plain to him that he's not wanted.

WRIGHT

[*To* LARKCOM.] Yes. You're good at "chipping" people. Make it uncomfortable for him.

LARKCOM

[*Nods and laughs.*] We'll have a bit of fun with him.

SAMUELS

Oh! leave him alone. He'll learn our wayth all right.

[CHRISTOPHER *has entered.*]

CHRISTOPHER

Unless we first learn his.

[VIVIAN, *who has been listening, turns round.*]

MRS. TOMPKINS

Learn his! [*Snorts indignantly.*]

MAJOR

[*With a snort—under his breath.*] Young puppy!

[KITE *has looked round.* LARKCOM *smokes.* JAPE *has glanced up.* WRIGHT *gives vent to a feeble sneer.* HOOLEY *is still dreaming.*]

VIVIAN

[STASIA *has just reached her with the coffee.*] No, thank you.

STASIA

Gar on. Do your 'eadache good.

VIVIAN

[*She looks at her and smiles; then takes it.*] Do you mind getting me my cloak? It's on the bed. Sure you don't mind?

STASIA

Not when you speak like that. [*She goes out.*]

MRS. TOMPKINS

Are you ready, dear?

VIVIAN

Yes. [*Rises.*] Stasia has just gone for my cloak.

MRS. TOMPKINS

[*Rising.*] You'll take care of her.

WRIGHT

[*Who has risen.*] That's all right.

MAJOR

[*Rises.*] That's all right. He'll take care of our little girl for us. [*He turns to his wife.*]

[VIVIAN *has come down.* WRIGHT *is standing near to her.*]

MAJOR

[*He indicates them with a wave of the hand. The fond tears are in his voice.*] May and—July.

LARKCOM

[*He springs up, and with half a dozen steps is at the piano. He thunders out Mendelssohn's Wedding March.*]

[THE MAJOR, *beaming, beats time with his hand and his head.* SAMUELS *has risen and moved round to the top of the table to look for new papers.* CHRISTOPHER *is also selecting a paper.* STASIA *has re-entered, with* VIVIAN'S *cloak.* WRIGHT *takes the cloak from* STASIA, *and puts it over* VIVIAN'S *shoulders.* MRS. SHARPE *enters. A screen of people has thus been formed, shutting off* VIVIAN'S *view. Behind it* THE STRANGER, *unnoticed, has entered. As* VIVIAN *turns to go out with* WRIGHT, THE STRANGER *stands before her. The quiet eyes are fixed on her—those eyes that seem to have seen all the sorrows of the world, great and little. The cloak falls from her shoulders to the floor about her feet. And a silence has also entered. The Wedding March dies away.*]

MRS. TOMPKINS

[*Who sees only* VIVIAN *rooted to the ground.*] What's the matter ?

VIVIAN

[*She turns her eyes to her mother.*] I am sorry. I cannot—I shall not be able to go to-night.

MAJOR

But, my dear !

VIVIAN

[*She turns again, her eyes upon* THE STRANGER.] I can't !—I can't !

THE STRANGER

[*He passes on.*]

VIVIAN

I'm sorry. [*To* WRIGHT.] Some other evening. [*Stooping swiftly, she picks up her cloak, wraps it tightly round her as one who is cold, and with bowed head passes hurriedly from the room.*]

MRS. TOMPKINS

It's the heat of the room. She hasn't been well all day. [*To the* MAJOR.] Don't you come. [*She follows* VIVIAN *out.*]

MRS. SHARPE

It *is* a bit close in here. Shall we have the window open ?

MISS KITE

I should like it.

STASIA

I'll see to it. [*She opens one of the windows, afterwards taking up the tray she had left on the desk. She goes out.*]

[SAMUELS, *having selected a newspaper, has re-seated himself.*]

MAJOR

[*To* WRIGHT.] Poor girl ! She'll be so dis-appointed.

[WRIGHT *answers with a snarl.*]

MAJOR

[*Coaxingly.*] Play you fifty up. Then we'll

see how she is. Can we have the table, Mrs. Sharpe ?

MRS. SHARPE

Certainly. I'll go and get it ready for you. [*She goes out.*]

MAJOR

Ah, thank you. [*Taking* WRIGHT'S *arm, he leads him out.*] Troublesome creatures, these girls !—troublesome creatures ! Yet what could we do without them ? What could we do—— [*He closes the door behind them.*]

[CHRISTOPHER *crosses and sits in easy-chair by fire. He makes to read ; but every now and again the paper drops ; he stares into the fire.*]

[MRS. DE HOOLEY *from time to time, leaning across, whispers to the* KITE *woman, who sometimes answers, but more often she is preoccupied, covertly watching* THE STRANGER. LARKCOM *has remained silent, watching events.*]

THE STRANGER

How well you play !

LARKCOM

[*He swings round on his stool.*] Hullo!—you there, old cockerlor—— [*He encounters* THE STRANGER'S *eyes. Somehow they put him out of countenance.*] Think so?

THE STRANGER

You have the touch of one who loves music.

LARKCOM

Here. [*He rises, grins up into* THE STRANGER'S *face.*] What's the little game? Want to borrow money?

THE STRANGER

You see, it would be of no use. You see through me at once.

LARKCOM

[THE STRANGER *is smiling. He turns away, ashamed of himself.*] Only my bit of fun. [*By way of explanation*] My weak spot—anybody telling me I know anything about music. Here of course—— [*With disgust*] Ah! All they understand here is "Tumpty, tumpty, tum."

THE STRANGER

And so you give them—what they understand.

LARKCOM

Oh well! somebody's got to do something to liven things up a bit.

THE STRANGER

Ah! yes. [*He puts a hand on the lad's shoulder.*] Some kind, good-natured body.

LARKCOM

Oh well! it comes easy—and I like doing it.

THE STRANGER

Yes.

LARKCOM

[*There is something about* THE STRANGER *that invites confidence.*] My idea was to have been an entertainer.

THE STRANGER

It was a good idea. You would have succeeded, I am sure.

LARKCOM

You see, I've got a voice.

THE STRANGER

And you have humour and a sense of fun. One reads it in your eyes.

LARKCOM

[*Suspicious for an instant—till he looks into* THE STRANGER'S *eyes.*] That's right. Why, sometimes—when I like to take the trouble—I'll have 'em all round me here, laughing. Not an easy crowd to start, mind you.

THE STRANGER

It is your vocation. It would be wrong of you to waste your gifts.

LARKCOM

Question is, would it pay ?

THE STRANGER

I think it would. And then, that is not the only question, is it ? You would be giving pleasure to so many.

LARKCOM

"Giving !" Here, don't you run away with the notion that Harry Larkcom is a philanthropist. What's it going to put into little Harry's money-box ? [*He slaps his pocket.*] That's the question little Harry always asks himself.

THE STRANGER

Always ? Are you sure ?

LARKCOM

Am I——

THE STRANGER

You play them "Tumpty, tumpty, tum." Why ?

LARKCOM

Why ! Because——

THE STRANGER

Does it give you any pleasure—you, a musician ! Does it add anything to the "money-box" ? [*The lad stares.*] No. You do it because you are just a good fellow. You will have them all around you, laughing. Wherever you are, life shall be a little brighter ; dull, tired faces shall be made to smile. You give them—so much more than money. You give them—yourself. Don't you call that being a philanthropist ?

LARKCOM

Of course, you can put it that way.

THE STRANGER

What other way ?

LARKCOM

I do like seeing people jolly round about me; hearing them whispering to one another that Harry Larkcom's the life and—— Gar on! Who are you getting at?—you and your philanthropists! I just like their admiration and applause. That's all I do it for.

THE STRANGER

Their gratitude, their appreciation. Are you not entitled to it ?

LARKCOM

You are determined——

THE STRANGER

The thanks of those you serve: that is the true "pay" of the artist.

LARKCOM

Here. Am I an artist now ?

THE STRANGER

And the artist is always a philanthropist, serving his fellow-men, not only for the sake of the money-box.

LARKCOM

I wonder. My old mother always would put it that way. "Harry's never so happy," she would say, "as when he's making other people happy."

THE STRANGER

Ah! she knew you. She would have been so proud of you.

LARKCOM

Well, it would be better than the sort of jobs I'm doing now.

THE STRANGER

You will forgive me. I have seen it so often. You artists are never content doing any other work than your own. All the rest is waste of time.

LARKCOM

Would you mind one day my trying over one or two little things of my own on you?

THE STRANGER

I should be delighted.

LARKCOM

Honour bright?

THE STRANGER

Honour bright! It will be pleasant—looking back—to think that I perhaps was of help to you in the beginning.

LARKCOM

Don't say anything about it to any of the others. [THE STRANGER *signifies understanding.*] "Harry Larkcom—artist!"

THE STRANGER

[*Smiling.*] And philanthropist.

LARKCOM

And philanthropist. [*Laughs.*] Good-night, in case I don't see you again—[*holds out his hand*]—partner.

THE STRANGER

Good-night, partner.

[LARKCOM *crosses.*]

SAMUELS

[*Stops him as he passes.*] Think he'th got any money ?

LARKCOM

Oh ! you find out for yourself.

SAMUELS

[*Rising.*] Ain't you learned anything ? What have you been talking about ?

LARKCOM

Want to know ? Art and philanthropy. [*Goes out, slamming the door.*]

SAMUELS

Art and—— ! Here, Henry. [*Follows him out.*]

[MRS. DE HOOLEY *has risen and put aside her work in its basket on the table.*]

CHRISTOPHER

[*Rising.*] Would you like this chair ?

MRS. DE HOOLEY

Thank you, I should have been glad of it earlier in the evening. [*Passes on.*]

MISS KITE

You're not going, dear ?

MRS. DE HOOLEY

Only to write a few letters. [*She seats herself at desk, her back to the room.*]

[CHRISTOPHER *takes* SAMUELS'S *vacated chair at table ; busies himself drawing sketches on the margins of newspapers.* THE STRANGER *has drawn near to where* MISS KITE *still sits.*]

MISS KITE

[*To* THE STRANGER, *indicating the vacant easy-chair opposite to her.*] Sit down. Talk to me.

[THE STRANGER *draws the chair nearer ; takes his seat.*]

MISS KITE

I am going to make you a confession. I'm afraid you'll think it fearfully bold of me. [*Giggles.*] But, you know, you interest me.

THE STRANGER

I am so glad. I wish so much to interest you.

MISS KITE

Now, that's a very pretty speech. I wonder if you really mean it. You men are so—— [*She raises her eyes, meaning to give him one of her "killing" glances. The* STRANGER'S *quiet, grave eyes are fixed on her. The giggle and the gush begin to fall from her.*] Why should you wish to interest me?

THE STRANGER

Because you are clever and witty. And the clever, witty woman can be so delightful a friend.

[*A silence.*]

MISS KITE

[*She is staring straight in front of her: a suddenly serious person.*] You think me clever, witty?

THE STRANGER

[*Smiling.*] You do not agree with me?

MISS KITE

[*Drily.*] You have made the discovery on a somewhat slight acquaintanceship. This is the first time we have spoken.

THE STRANGER

But I have had the privilege of listening. You should not talk before those from whom you wish to keep it a secret.

MISS KITE

I—— [*She smiles—she cannot help it.*] I did not think you were listening so attentively. [*She turns to him with sudden anxiety.*] I hope you didn't think that I was at all—at all spiteful, in any of my remarks?

THE STRANGER

A little—caustic. It is a mistake witty talkers so often make. You could afford to do without it.

MISS KITE

[*Looking into the fire again.*] I suppose one grows bitter as one grows old. [*Remembering herself*] I mean, of course—— [THE STRANGER'S *eyes confuse her.*]

THE STRANGER

But you have not even that excuse. You are not old.

MISS KITE

Well, I'm—[*she struggles, but* THE STRANGER'S *eyes insist upon the truth*]—I'm forty. You don't call that young, do you?

THE STRANGER

Young enough not to have forgotten the thoughts of youth; old enough to have learnt pity. Forty! Why that is a beautiful age.

MISS KITE

[*She is angry with* THE STRANGER, *with herself.*] Oh yes, I dare say. Any age, I expect, *you* would think beautiful. Perhaps you think *I* am beautiful.

THE STRANGER

[*Gravely looking at her.*] Yes, I think you are beautiful—quite beautiful. But you have one failing that mars it.

MISS KITE

[*Snappishly.*] Hadn't you better tell me of it? Pity it should be marred by just one failing. I might be able to correct it.

THE STRANGER

It is lack of vanity. [*She glances suspiciously. Is he making game of her?*] You look into your glass and are, quite needlessly, dissatisfied with yourself. It is—forgive me—so foolish of you.

MISS KITE

[*She turns her eyes from him.*] You mean you would like me better without the paint and the powder—and the dye.

THE STRANGER

I think that you yourself—I may draw the picture?—a graceful, comely woman, perhaps a little pale—there are white roses and red—with delicate features on which the sculptor Thought has chiselled his fine lines, giving to them character, distinction; her still-bright eyes unspoilt; with her fit crown of soft brown hair that Time has touched with no unkindly hand—would be the more beautiful.

MISS KITE

[*Her eyes still turned away from him.*] You don't understand. The world makes life hard to —old women.

THE STRANGER

Will you not help them ? [*She turns her eyes to his.*] By letting the world see that "old women" of forty [*he is smiling*] can be charming.

MISS KITE

[*She rises.*] Good-night.

THE STRANGER

[*Rising also.*] You are going ?

MISS KITE

To try to forget all that you have been saying. Yes, I can—and I mean to. I'm a spiteful, venomous-tongued old cat—a painted, pitiful creature without self-respect—and I hate you because you have made me see myself as I am. I hate you. I——

[*The folding doors open.* WRIGHT *and the* MAJOR *enter.* MISS KITE *has restrained her angry tones to a whisper.* MRS. DE HOOLEY *has continued her writing,* CHRISTOPHER *his sketching.*]

MAJOR

[*As they enter.*] Ah ! you're too good for me.

WRIGHT

You weren't up to your usual form.

MAJOR

Ah ! I'm no good against a player like you. [*To* CHRISTOPHER] Any news from upstairs ?

CHRISTOPHER

[*Shakes his head.*] None.

MISS KITE

[*She has recovered her old self. She speaks to impress the room.*] I have enjoyed our little talk *so* much. Good-night.

THE STRANGER

Good-night. [*He holds out his hand. She answers by flouncing out of the room.*]

MAJOR

[*To* WRIGHT.] I'll run up—see what's happening. [*Finds himself in front of* THE STRANGER ; *he stops, spreads out his legs, puts his hands behind him, and stares insultingly.*] Well, what's going to pull off the Lincolnshire Handicap ! Tell me, and I'll go straight out and bet my boots upon it.

THE STRANGER

I think you would be ill advised. I am not an authority.

MAJOR

Not a—Aren't you Captain Spy of the "Racing News"?

THE STRANGER

I have not that distinction.

MAJOR

God bless my soul! They told me you were Captain Spy, travelling incognito. [*Beginning a coarse laugh, he looks round the room for support. It is not forthcoming. The joke has fallen strangely flat.*] Shan't be long. [*He strides out, banging the door behind him.*]

WRIGHT

He always will have his little joke.

THE STRANGER

A sense of humour is a delightful trait at all times.

WRIGHT

I want to ask you a question. [*He looks round,*

draws THE STRANGER *further aside.*] "Heat of the room" be damned. It was the moment she caught sight of you that she changed—suddenly discovered that she wasn't feeling well [*with a sneering laugh.*] What's the understanding between you two?

THE STRANGER

You think it was I who influenced her?

WRIGHT

I don't *think* anything at all about it. I was watching. Her eyes were fixed on yours all the time.

THE STRANGER

May it not have been merely her Better Self pleading to her?

WRIGHT

Her Better Self! What better can she do for herself than marry me? I'm rich. Ain't I going to be kind to her? Ain't I going to settle money on her—money on herself, to spend as she likes? [*With increasing vehemence*] Ain't I good enough for her?

THE STRANGER

And she? Would she have been good enough for you?

WRIGHT

[*Puzzled.*] She! Good enough for me!

THE STRANGER

Taking all your gifts—your love. Giving you nothing in return but the cold embraces of a shameless woman.

[*A silence.*]

WRIGHT

You don't understand. The world ain't a story-book—all Jacks and Jills and love in a cottage. The girl's got to live.

THE STRANGER

Ay! To live! It is a fine thing to live! [*He turns again smiling to little Old Joey.*] You shall give her Life!

WRIGHT

[*Staring.*] Give her Life?

THE STRANGER

The lad she loves. [*Old Joey darts a glance at* CHRISTOPHER, *where he sits all unconscious.*] She shall cleave to him, cherish him. She shall be the mother of children—children who shall crown her brows with honour! Love! Labour! That is Life to a woman. You shall give her Life!

[*Again a silence.*]

WRIGHT

[*Peevishly.*] All jolly fine. What about me? Where do I come in?

THE STRANGER

Man, you love her?

WRIGHT

Yes, I know I do.

THE STRANGER

Then it is all quite simple. There is nothing else to think of but what is best—for her.

WRIGHT

Yes, there is. There's me. Ain't I got any rights?

THE STRANGER

Ah, yes. The right to serve.

WRIGHT

Here, you're making a mistake. You're talking to me as if I were some high and mighty Knight Errant sort of a chap. It's silly of you. I ain't even a gentleman. I'm only a common little old man. Why, I was a bookmaker—that's all I was. You know, a betting man—a bit shady at that. Daresay it's all right what you say. Only [*he taps his breast ; his voice has risen to a plaintive whine ; Self-pity has given to it pathos*] I ain't got it in me.

THE STRANGER

Are you sure it is I who am making the mistake ?

WRIGHT

[*He makes a gesture of the hands, and, shaking his head, creeps to the easy-chair. Sits crouching with his hands stretched out to the fire.*]

THE STRANGER

You are so sure, [*smiling*] " Sir Joseph ! "

WRIGHT

[*He turns.*] How did you know that used to be my nickname?

THE STRANGER

You were a public character. Wherever you went, men spoke of you—of your fine lordly ways, of your wondrous kindness. Women also.

WRIGHT

Flinging your money about a bit when you've got plenty of it, that ain't the same as giving up the woman you love.

THE STRANGER

Forgetting Self—forgetting all things but the loving of her, and the serving of her! Ah yes, he would be a great gentleman who could do that. You—you do not feel yourself quite equal to it?

WRIGHT

[*He turns a poor, troubled face towards* THE STRANGER.] Why mightn't she come to love me—in time? I would be good to her—and kind—and—— [*The quiet eyes are fixed on him. The foolish words die away.*]

THE STRANGER

I think you could win her love more readily. So that she would think of you to the end always with deep wonder—teach your name to her children that they, too, might learn to love and honour it.

[*A silence reigns, broken only by the scratching of the* HOOLEY *pen. Then the door opens, and the* MAJOR *reappears.*]

MAJOR

[*Looking round, he does not at first see* WRIGHT.] Is he gone? [*Coming further into the room, he discovers him.*] Ah! there you are. I'm afraid the dear child will not be able——

WRIGHT

[*He seems to have suddenly grown older, feebler. A new note of gentleness, of humbleness, has changed his voice. He puts the other aside with a quiet gesture.*] Tell her it doesn't matter. Tell her not to—trouble. [*He rises and goes slowly towards the door.*]

[MRS. DE HOOLEY, *having finished her letters, has risen.* CHRISTOPHER *looks up from his work.* THE STRANGER *stands near the littered table.*]

WRIGHT

[*He turns.*] Pity to waste the ticket. [*He draws the theatre voucher from his waistcoat pocket—looks from one to other.*] Would anybody care for it?

[JAPE SAMUELS *has entered with papers of a prospectus order in his hand.*]

[*To the* MAJOR] Would you? Do you think Mrs. Tompkins might like to go?

MAJOR

Well—[*he looks at his watch*]—well, yes, it's very kind of you. Perhaps she might.

WRIGHT

[*As he gives it to him.*] It's a nice little box—for two.

MAJOR

Very kind of you—very kind of you indeed.

WRIGHT

That's all right.

[*He turns again, and the little bent old figure passes slowly out.* MRS. DE HOOLEY, *taking her work-basket from the table, seats herself by the fire.* SAMUELS *remains standing.*]

MAJOR

Umph! Seems a bit down in the mouth, our poor friend.

SAMUELS

[*With a laugh.*] Not the evening he exthpected.

MAJOR

Ah, we lovers of women!—how we suffer!

[SAMUELS *laughs.*]

MAJOR

[*To* THE STRANGER.] Not a married man yourself, sir?

THE STRANGER

I have not that happiness.

MAJOR

Ah! I sympathise with you, sir. I sympathise. [*He is exchanging grimaces with* JAPE, *wonderfully pleased with his own clowning.*] Been married myself four-and-twenty years. Regretted it—only once.

[SAMUELS *laughs again.*]

MAJOR

What are you laughing at? It's quite right—once, and once only.

[SAMUELS *becomes convulsed.*]

MAJOR

[*To* THE STRANGER.] These modern young men, they ridicule all sentiment. They laugh at us—call us "Darby and Joan"; can't understand a man being in love with his own wife.

THE STRANGER

They have many things to learn.

MAJOR

Exactly what I tell them. Star of my life, I call her, sir—always there, shining down upon me, beaming, twinkling——

[JAPE *is guffawing,* MRS. DE HOOLEY *smiling,* CHRISTOPHER *watching.*]

THE STRANGER

[*He interrupts, with a gesture.*] I remember her well—as a girl.

MAJOR

[*He suddenly drops his clowning.*] You !—Re——Who are you ?

THE STRANGER

A friend you have forgotten.

[JAPE *seats himself ; busies himself with his papers.* MRS. DE HOOLEY *and* CHRISTOPHER *take up their work again.*]

MAJOR

I beg your pardon. My memory for faces, I am sorry to say——

THE STRANGER

It was a long while ago.

MAJOR

It is very good of you to find excuse. [*He is puzzled. He keeps eyeing* THE STRANGER *from under his brows. He is trying to recollect, but failing.*] It will all come back to me, I have no doubt. Meanwhile, I thank you, sir, for recalling yourself. Mrs. Tompkins will also, I am sure, be pleased that you have done her the honour to remember her.

THE STRANGER

To have forgotten her would have been still more difficult, would it not? [*He is smiling.*]

MAJOR

It is kind of you, sir, to say so.

THE STRANGER

The evening we first met her! [*The* MAJOR *glances swiftly.*] By the stepping-stones! It was hawthorn-time, you remember? Could any vision have been sweeter?

MAJOR

[*After a short silence, very drily.*] Yes, yes, she was a dainty little piece of goods [*he turns away*]—in those days.

THE STRANGER

It is rather wonderful—you will not be jealous of an old admirer—how lightly time has dealt with her.

MAJOR

Yes, she has kept her good looks—to a great extent. Of course her figure——

THE STRANGER

[*He interrupts again, smiling.*] A little fuller. A fault in the right direction, is it not ?

MAJOR

Yes, yes, I suppose it is. Never could myself abide a scraggy woman.

THE STRANGER

You also—if you will allow me—have worn well, sir.

MAJOR

[*He turns quickly*]. You think so.

THE STRANGER

The years will take their toll. But I find still the same quick, youthful step, the same—how may I say it ?—the same gallant jauntiness.

MAJOR

[*Laughing, delighted.*] Still the soldier, eh ? Still the soldier !

THE STRANGER

I think it was that gave you an unfair advantage. The women ! they succumb so easily to a uniform.

MAJOR

[*Swaggering, laughing.*] Well, yes. There is something about us that seems to appeal to them—eh ?

THE STRANGER

The soldier's reputation—for chivalry, for tenderness, no doubt.

MAJOR

[*The conceit falls from him. He glances suspiciously at* THE STRANGER ; *fidgets, turns away.*] Very possibly.

THE STRANGER

A few of the older folks shook their heads. But some of the younger women, I remember, frankly confessed that they envied her.

MAJOR

Um ! Ah, yes ! [*He laughs, awkwardly.*]

[*The door opens.* MRS. TOMPKINS *enters, an open letter in her hand. She has come downstairs, as she herself would express it, to "have it out." She thrusts the letter forward.*]

MRS. TOMPKINS

So! So, my dressmaker, in future——

MAJOR

Ah! my dear, you are just in time. [*She is about to speak. His look, the tones of his voice, his vehement whisper, as he waves the letter aside, silence her.*] Another time—another time I tell you. [*Then aloud.*] I want to introduce you to an old friend of ours. [*He indicates* THE STRANGER.] A friend who remembers us, I am ashamed to say, better than we seem to have remembered him; a friend who knew us long ago—in our courting days.

MRS. TOMPKINS

[*Bewildered at the* MAJOR'S *manner, she looks at* THE STRANGER *long and hard. The dawn of some strange recollection comes to her. She turns a puzzled, questioning face to her husband; then looks again at* THE STRANGER, *then back to her husband.*] Yes. It was long ago—when I was a girl—in Devonshire. [*Her eyes are still fixed on* THE STRANGER. *The recollection grows.*] We used to have long talks together. I remember.

THE STRANGER

Your lover—if I may take him at his word [*he turns to the* MAJOR; *smiling, lays his hand on his shoulder*]—has been telling me how happily your marriage has turned out. [THE STRANGER *stands between them, smiling. She turns her eyes upon her husband. He seeks to cover his confusion with a jerky laugh. Tries to find something to say; can think of nothing.*] May I—a little late—offer my congratulations? In the world's book, so full of the vulgar stories of dead love, it is pleasant to come across one with the old-fashioned ending.

[MRS. TOMPKINS *remains silent. The* MAJOR *is much relieved.*]

MAJOR

"The old-fashioned ending." [*Laughs.*] Very good—very good indeed. They married and lived happy—— [*The theatre voucher is still in his hand. It catches his eye.*] Ah! I was forgetting. Mr. Wright has been kind enough to suggest, my dear, that you and I should make use of his box for to-night. What do you think?

[*The door is open.* MRS. SHARPE *has entered. She stands watching.*]

MRS. TOMPKINS

[*She is bewildered—not quite sure whether she is awake or dreaming.*] Yes, yes; I'd be rather glad to—to get out. I—I shall only be a minute. I have only my cloak to put on. [*She turns to go.*]

MAJOR

[*The idea occurs to him, Heaven knows since how long. It fits awkwardly on him.*] Can—can I get it for you, my dear?

[SAMUELS *gives vent to a low laugh.*]

MAJOR

[*Turns on him fiercely, having perhaps expected something of the kind.*] I beg pardon, sir. I failed to catch your remark.

SAMUELS

[*Bewildered, frightened.*] I never thaid anything.

MAJOR

My mistake, sir. [*He turns again to his wife.*] Can I—find it, do you think, my dear?

MRS. TOMPKINS

[*She has been staring. On her also forgotten ways fit ill.*] I think I left it upstairs. Thank you, John.

[*The* MAJOR *goes on his errand.*]

[*The astonished* JAPE *rises, and, whistling, crosses to the desk, where, having lit another cigar, he sits and works.* MRS. SHARPE *goes to the little work-table, where she pretends to look for some work, but her eyes are on the centre of the room.* CHRISTOPHER *and* MRS. DE HOOLEY *cast glances.*]

MRS. TOMPKINS

So it has turned out happily—he told you that.

THE STRANGER

That they call you "Darby and Joan." [*She looks at him.*] Nothing, it seems to me, is more beautiful than the love that has weathered the storms of life. The blossom that flowers in the heart of the young, as in those days when first you met him, so handsome, so kind, you remember?—that too, is beautiful, the love of the young for the young. It is the beginning of life. But the love of the—forgive me—of the old for the old, that is the beginning of things longer.

MRS. TOMPKINS

Yes, I remember your voice : it was always the same. [*She turns and looks at him.*] But it is you only I seem to remember—nothing about you—no time, no place. I suppose it will come back to me.

THE STRANGER

And if not, we will not trouble. The meeting-place of friends is in the heart.

MRS. TOMPKINS

[*She looks at him, smiling.*] You always thought well of me. I remember that.

THE STRANGER

I knew you—so well.

[*The* MAJOR *re-enters with the cloak. He has donned an Inverness cape and carries his hat and gloves.*]

MAJOR

[*He places the cloak around her.*] We shall just

be in time. [*To* THE STRANGER.] I shall see you again, sir. We must talk about old days.

THE STRANGER

[*Smiling.*] And grow young.

[*The* MAJOR *laughs.*]

MRS. TOMPKINS

[*To* THE STRANGER, *as nervously and doubtfully she takes the* MAJOR'S *arm.*] Good-night.

THE STRANGER

Good-night.

MRS. TOMPKINS

[*At door.*] Oh, I wonder—shall I want my smelling-salts ?

MAJOR

My dear, [*patting his pocket*] I thought of it.

[*She smiles at him. They go out. The* MAJOR *closes the door behind them.*]

SAMUELS

[*So soon as the door is closed, he turns round in his chair and bursts into a laugh.*] Well, if that don't—[*laughs again*]—if that don't take——

MRS. SHARPE

[*With some work in her hand she has crossed over. To* JAPE, *interrupting him*] Can you see to work here? Shall I get you some candles?

SAMUELS

[*He accepts the interruption.*] Vell, yeth. One ith a bit in oneth own light. Thankth. [*Speaking low*] I thay——

MRS. SHARPE

[*Cuts him short.*] I will get them for you. [*She goes out.*]

SAMUELS

[*Seeing there is no one to join in his laughter, he shrugs his shoulders and turns his face to the desk.*] Ageth of miraclthes begun again.

[THE STRANGER *is standing with his hands stretched out towards the fire.*]

MRS. DE HOOLEY

It is curious your having known the Major and Mrs. Tompkins. Because I can't help fancying that *we* also are friends.

THE STRANGER

I wonder !

MRS. DE HOOLEY

Each time I hear your voice it comes home to me more and more that we have met somewhere.

THE STRANGER

[*He looks at her.*] Yes, you are right.

MRS. DE HOOLEY

I was sure of it. Do you know where I think it was ? At the Tatton-Jones's ?

THE STRANGER

It was not at the Tatton-Jones's.

MRS. DE HOOLEY

You are sure ? The Yorkshire branch ? Her grandfather was Groom of the Bedchamber to William the Fourth.

THE STRANGER

Quite sure.

MRS. DE HOOLEY

[*Tries again.*] My cousin, Sir George Tweedle, Bart., has scarcely any one on his visiting-list who has not a title. So it could hardly have been there?

THE STRANGER

Hardly.

MRS. DE HOOLEY

I wonder, could it have been at the Eghams's—the Hampshire Eghams's? He married a niece of Lord Bath.

THE STRANGER

It was not at the Eghams's.

MRS. DE HOOLEY

[*She is sure that this time she has it right. She smiles with confidence.*] At Drayton Towers—Lady Mitcham's place.

THE STRANGER

Nor at Drayton Towers.

MRS. DE HOOLEY

It is curious—very curious. I feel so confident——

THE STRANGER

It was before you came down in the world.

MRS. DE HOOLEY

[*She stares at him, but the grave, quiet eyes tell nothing.*] Before I came down—— [*The rest is speechlessness.*]

THE STRANGER

In the days when you were a great lady.

MRS. DE HOOLEY

I—I don't understand.

THE STRANGER

Each evening, after the long day's labour in the factory, your work-worn hands so tired, you climbed the many creaking stairs to bring help and comfort to one all others had forsaken.

[*A silence.*]

MRS. DE HOOLEY

[*She has risen. She looks round fearfully.*] It—it didn't matter in those days. I—I was nobody.

THE STRANGER

You held high rank with noble men and women, then.

MRS. DE HOOLEY

I—I know what you mean, of course. But you—you don't understand. When one is—is called upon to enter Society—— [*She looks at him; there is something in his eyes that stays her.*]

THE STRANGER

One leaves one's womanhood behind?

MRS. DE HOOLEY

[*After a moment's silence.*] One—one isn't expected to drag after one a sister who—who brought disgrace upon herself.

THE STRANGER

Your cloak shall hide her wounds.

MRS. DE HOOLEY

[*The poor worried lady is beginning to cry.*] I—I did quite a good deal for her. I did my Duty—[*she draws herself up*] till it became impossible!

THE STRANGER

Ah yes! Duty so soon tires. [*She is still crying, her eyes downcast. His hand rests on hers a moment.*] Love goes all the way. [*She looks up.*]

[*The door opens.* MRS. SHARPE *enters, bearing a lighted candle in each hand. She pauses a moment, looks from* THE STRANGER *to* MRS. HOOLEY, *then passes on, places the candles on the desk.*]

MRS. DE HOOLEY

[*She gathers her work. The tears have gone ; the face is smiling.*] So you thought me a great lady, in those days ?

THE STRANGER

A great lady. It is the Helpless and the Fallen that hold in their hands the patents of nobility.

[*She goes towards the door, turns, smiles back at him, then passes out.*]

SAMUELS

[*Without looking up.*] Want to have a talk with you, my lady, about my little bill. [*Turning on her.*] What do you mean by——

MRS. SHARPE

[*Staying him by a pleading gesture.*] I am sorry. For one or two items, I know, I have overcharged you. I will make you out a new one. [*She moves away.*]

SAMUELS

[*Looks after her—shakes his head.*] Thomething very wrong going on here. [*He turns once more to his labour.*] Hope it ain't anything catching.

MRS. SHARPE

[*She goes to the table, her idea being to fold and rearrange the journals. But the second or third she takes up has upon its margin the sketches* CHRISTOPHER *has been making. She pauses with it in her hand.*] You have been drawing our portraits.

CHRISTOPHER

[*He is still sketching, his head bent over his work. With a light laugh.*] Yes ; just amusing myself.

MRS. SHARPE

They are wonderful ! So like ! And yet——

CHRISTOPHER

[*The tone of her voice strikes him. He glances up.*] Yet what ? What is wrong with them ? [*He stretches out his hand for the paper. She gives it to him : the wonder comes to him also.*] Did *I* draw these ?

MRS. SHARPE

Who else ?

CHRISTOPHER

But what is the meaning of it ? These are the faces of beautiful men and women !

THE STRANGER

[*Unnoticed, he has drawn near.*] Are not all men and women beautiful ? Was the model amiss ?

CHRISTOPHER

Ah ! I must have been thinking of him. They were his very words—my master, who first taught me. "Ugliness," he would always say, "it is but skin deep. The business of Art is to reveal the beauty underlying all things." Your voice reminds me of him.

[MRS. SHARPE *goes out unnoticed.*]

THE STRANGER

Then I have been of service to you ?

CHRISTOPHER

[*The enthusiasm dies out.*] I am not so sure of

that. I was trying to forget him. [*He rises and moves away.*] He expected great things of me.

THE STRANGER

[*He has remained, his hand upon the drawings. He raises one, looks from it to the lad.*] He was wrong ?

CHRISTOPHER

Ah, if one could only be an artist without being a man ! [*He turns, with a twitching smile.*] You see, sir, we young men—we want to live as well as work—[*turning away again*]—to live ! to love !

THE STRANGER

And Love and Art may not be comrades ?

CHRISTOPHER

Art doesn't pay, sir, and one's Love [*with a short, bitter laugh*] demands to be kept, at least in comfort.

THE STRANGER

"Demands" ? Love gives, not asks.

CHRISTOPHER

[*With a gesture.*] Ah, *that* Love !

THE STRANGER

Is there another ?

CHRISTOPHER

[*He turns with an appealing gesture.*] What can I do ? I want her. Can I ask her to share poverty ?

THE STRANGER

You would ask her to share shame—the reward of the traitor ?

CHRISTOPHER

" Traitor " ?

THE STRANGER

To your Art ; [*he lays his hand again upon the drawing*] to the great gift that has been entrusted to you !

CHRISTOPHER

You take a high view of Art. [*It is, without his meaning it, a sneer.*]

THE STRANGER

[*There is sternness in the voice—the look.*] Since when have *you* taken a low one ?

[*A silence.*]

CHRISTOPHER

[*He turns.*] Thank you, sir. It *is* a great gift. [*Then sadly*] I am not worthy of it.

THE STRANGER

Worthy—who knows ?—to suffer for it. It is a great privilege to be deemed worthy to suffer. Art, also, has its cross.

CHRISTOPHER

[*Smiling.*] I wish, sir, I were as young as you seem to be. *I* had such thoughts—once. [*With another laugh*] I have always sought to put them away from me as something to be ashamed of.

THE STRANGER

It is the thoughts of youth that shall one day make the world young. I may come up, some time, and see your pictures ?

CHRISTOPHER

To-morrow, sir. It will be so kind of you. To-night—I am making a fire. [*Smiling at* THE STRANGER, *he goes out.*]

SAMUELS

[*He hears the click of the closing door. He looks*

round shyly. THE STRANGER'S *back is towards him.*]

SAMUELS

[*The cunning creeps into his face. He sits for a few moments working out his plan : a few slight movements of the hands, a little scratching and smoothing of the evil face. Then he blows out the two candles, and, with his papers in his hand, softly rises and comes across.* THE STRANGER *turns ; and for a moment, in face of those strange eyes,* JAPE'S *brazenness deserts him. Then, recovering himself, he thrusts his face forward, leering, but meaning to be amiable.*] Don't want to make your fortune, do you ?

THE STRANGER

Do not all men ?

SAMUELS

Got thomething here thath going to make mine. I'm going to be a millionaire. Got a thilver mine here— [*he strikes the papers with his hand*]—worth —I'm tho exthited about it, I go about telling everybody I meet. [*Laughs.*] Of courth they don't believe me.

THE STRANGER

Why should they not ?

SAMUELS

Well, it ain't thenth, ith it ? If a fellow hath got hold of a good thing, he keepth it to himthelf —doethn't want to let a lot of other people into it.

THE STRANGER

It depends upon the "fellow." There are generous fellows who love to share their good fortune with their friends.

SAMUELS

[*He looks at* THE STRANGER ; *grows bolder.*] Jutht exthactly what I thay. Why not thare with your palth ? Ethpethally when—ath in thith cath—thereth enough for all. [*All the time he is eyeing* THE STRANGER, *advancing from point to point.*] Would you *like* a thmall parthel ? [*He opens his papers, pushes them across the table towards* THE STRANGER.] *You'd* do good with the money. I can thee that. For a mere couple of hundred—— Here, don't lithen to me. Look at the figurth for yourthelf. They'll thow you. [*He seats himself the other side of the table.*]

THE STRANGER

[*With a gentle movement he pushes them back across the table.*] You are—is it not so?—a Jew?

SAMUELS

[*He starts back as though struck. With snarling anger*] Vell, what if I am? You can't help what you wath born. Ath a matter of fact, I ain't a Jew—not now. And if I wath, what differenth would that make?

THE STRANGER

Your word would be sufficient.

[SAMUELS *stares.*]

THE STRANGER

The word of a Jew.

[*A silence.*]

SAMUELS

What makth you thay that?

THE STRANGER

So many of the noblest men I have known, men I have loved, [*a far-away thought is in his eyes*] have been Jews. It is a great race—a race rich in honourable names.

SAMUELS

[*He is hard at work thinking.*] Yet to hear the way they talk and thneer, you'd think there wath thomething dithgrathful in even having been born a Jew.

THE STRANGER

The Jew shall teach them their mistake.

SAMUELS

[*He glances up—fidgets in his chair.*] Of courthe, I don't thay that thome among uth mayn't be a bit tricky.

THE STRANGER

There are to be found everywhere those not ashamed to bring dishonour on their people.

SAMUELS

[*He rises.*] Jutht exthactly what I thay. Thereth good and bad everywhere. We're no worthe than anybody elthe. We can hold our own—I don't thay ath we can't. If it'th a game of who'th going to betht whom—very well, we're *in* it. If a thentleman cometh to uth, treath uth *ath* a thentleman——

THE STRANGER

He will find that the Jew can also be a gentleman. [*A moment—he touches lightly the papers.*] You were going to be so kind——

SAMUELS

[*He stares at* THE STRANGER, *then at his wonderful papers, then again at* THE STRANGER.] Yeth, I did —— What do you think about it—yourthelf ?

THE STRANGER

That your offer is most generous—that I accept it, with all thanks.

SAMUELS

[*He is still staring at* THE STRANGER.] Don't you think—you'll forgive my thaying it, but you don't thtrike me exthactly ath a buthineth man —don't you think it would be better to leave it over for a day or two ?—conthult a friend ?

THE STRANGER

What friend better than yourself

SAMUELS

[*Slowly he draws back the papers.*] Got mythelf to think of. Wath forgetting that. You thee, if you wath to take my word and anything by any chanthe wath to go wrong, *I* thould feel—[*Laughs, then gravely*] well, I thould feel ath though I'd been thelling the whole Jewith rathe for a couple of hundred poundth or tho. 'Tain't worth it. [*He moves towards the door—turns.*] Thorry. Thomething elthe, perhapth—thome other time.

[*He goes out, closing the door.*]

[THE STRANGER *remains standing by the table. The folding doors open.* STASIA *enters. A yet further improvement has taken place in her. She has been "titivating" herself. She wears* LARKCOM'S *gaudy green glass earrings.*]

STASIA

[*She crosses behind the table. Her eyes are drawn towards* THE STRANGER.] Only looked in to see if the fire was all right. Nothing I can do for you, before I go to bed ?

THE STRANGER

You are gaily adorned.

STASIA

[*Puzzled at first, then understanding.*] What, these ? [*with a movement of her hands to the great earrings*]. They ain't mine—not exactly—not yet. Just put them on to see 'ow they suited me.

THE STRANGER

They are not good enough for you.

STASIA

Of course they are not real. I know that. But they're rather effective, don't you think ? [*She looks up at him with her serious, childish eyes.*]

THE STRANGER

They do not become you. They are not pure.

STASIA

What can I expect ? You see, I'm only a slavey.

THE STRANGER

Your people—who are they ?

STASIA

My people ! Do you mean relations—father, mother, all that sort o' thing ?

THE STRANGER

Who are they ?

STASIA

[*Shakes her head.*] I dunno. My mother died in the 'orspital, so they've always told me. Never 'eard anything about my father.

THE STRANGER

[*He lays his hand upon her shoulder.*] He was a friend of mine.

STASIA

[*Her great eyes open wide.*] My father !—a friend of—— [*Her voice dies away in the wonder.*]

THE STRANGER

A dear friend.

STASIA

Then—then was he a gentleman ?

THE STRANGER

[*He remains silent a moment before speaking.*] A great gentleman.

STASIA

[*The marvel growing.*] Then am I—a lidy ?

THE STRANGER

His daughter. And so like him. [*He puts his hands upon her shoulders, smiling at her.*] His kind, brave eyes——

STASIA

[*She is looking up at him, smiling.*]

THE STRANGER

His ever-ready smile—his voice!

STASIA

[*As in a dream.*] And he was—a gentleman?

THE STRANGER

A gallant gentleman. [*He turns away a moment.*] May his sins be forgot!

STASIA

And I—— [*Then from her dream she wakes.*] You're making gime of me. [*The tears are in her voice.*] 'Ow can I be any one? I was born in a workhouse.

THE STRANGER

[*Again a moment's silence.*] A King, once, was born in a stable.

STASIA

Yus. Sort o' King like I'm a lidy—that nobody knows.

THE STRANGER

They learnt it later.

STASIA

[*She looks up—meets his eyes.*] You're talking sense: you mean a real King—with a crown.

THE STRANGER

Yes; He wore a crown. So, you see, Stasia, the place doesn't matter. There must be poor kings the world, for a time, does not know. So there must likewise be poor gentlewomen, daughters of poor gentlemen.

STASIA

[*She looks at him and the doubts fall away.*] Yes, he must have been a gentleman if he was your friend. [*She smiles, and her hands creep out timidly towards him.*] Would you mind—for his sake, like? I've often thought I'd like to have a friend.

THE STRANGER

[*He stands waiting. His arms are open.*]

STASIA

[*She comes towards him, smiling. Then suddenly she stops, and a frightened, hunted look comes into her eyes.*] No. I beg your pardon; I was forgetting. I'm a bad 'un.

THE STRANGER

[*But he still stands, waiting, his arms open.*]

STASIA

[*She shakes her head.*] You don't understand. I'm a bad 'un.

THE STRANGER

Did I ask you?

STASIA

You mean it don't matter? You can——[*Step by step she has reached him.*]

THE STRANGER

[*He puts his arms about her.*]

STASIA

[*She looks up into his face, her childish eyes filled with love.*] I didn't know.

THE STRANGER

[*He, bending over her, kisses her; then gently puts her from him.*] Good-night.

STASIA

[*She takes from her ears the earrings. Throws them one after the other into the fire. They fall with a faint crash.*] Good-night. [*Looking back, smiling, she goes out.*]

[*The dim gas-jets give but a faint, cold light.* THE STRANGER *sits in the large chair that is near to the table. The fire-glow shines upon his face.*]

[*After a while the door opens, and* VIVIAN *enters, closing it behind her. She has changed back into the plain black dress she wore in the afternoon. Her hair, drawn back from her white face, she has allowed to fall loose. She moves slowly across the room, looking at* THE STRANGER *without speaking. She kneels the other side of the fire, her arm over the arm of the chair, staring into the fire. After a while she turns her face and looks at him.*]

VIVIAN

Who are you? Why do you follow me? I see you in the streets; you look at me out of crowds. Why have you come here? What is it that you want with me?

THE STRANGER

To plead with you—will you listen?—for one who loves you.

VIVIAN

You are his friend. It is he who has brought you here—to plead for him. Poor boy! [*Then hardening again.*] Well, what have you to say? What proposals do you bring from him? What does my lover offer me?

THE STRANGER

Poverty—struggle; hopes—fears; pain—joy; love—life.

[*A silence.*]

VIVIAN

[*With her bitter laugh.*] So he has told you I am that—that sort of a woman? Hadn't you better find out the truth about me before you waste your words? Look at me [*she draws nearer*] with those eyes that seem to read one through and through. Is it not written plainly enough, the thing I am?

THE STRANGER

[*He looks into her eyes.*] A woman fair and sweet, made for honour, for worship.

VIVIAN

[*With a low cry.*] Ah, perhaps! But what has she made of herself? What else do you read?

THE STRANGER

It is not written.

VIVIAN

[*She springs up, with a mocking laugh.*] But it soon will be. Shall I tell you the lover of my choice? The man who can give me all my soul's desire—money and the things that money can buy. You think me a woman. I am only a luxury-loving animal. He will give me Shame to live with me. But after a little while I shall get used to her. She will be clad in fine clothes, and I shall think her Honour. Go back to him. Tell him my choice is made. I have had a better offer. I marry Shame.

THE STRANGER

You will not wed with Shame. You shall not.

VIVIAN

[*She turns.*] "Shall not"? Who will stay me?

THE STRANGER

[*He rises.*] Your Better Self.

[*A silence.*]

There are they whose Better Self lies slain—slain by their own hand to trouble them no more. But yours, child, you have let grow too strong. It will ever be your master. You must obey. Flee from it, it will ever follow you. You cannot escape it. Insult it, and it will chastise you with burning thoughts, with stinging self-reproach, with repentance that comes too late. It is your master. You must obey. [*The sternness dies, the gentleness returns. He lays his hand upon her.*] You will marry your lover. With him you will walk the way of sunlight and of shadow.

VIVIAN

Who are you? I know your voice. I hear it in the wind. I hear it in the silence of the night.

Who—— [*She is standing, her face illumined by the firelight, looking at him. His face is not seen. There comes a strange awe into her eyes—into her voice. With a cry*] You are—— [*There is a movement as though she were about to kneel.*]

[THE STRANGER *stretches out his hands and stays her.*]

[*The stage has grown dark. There is a long, strange silence.*]

THE STRANGER

A fellow-lodger. Good-night.

[*She stands still gazing at him with that strange look of awe, her face illumined by the fire.* THE STRANGER'S *face is not seen.*]

THE CURTAIN FALLS

CHARACTERS IN THE EPILOGUE

An Old Bachelor
Two Lovers
A Husband and Wife
A Jew
An Entertaining Party
A Maiden Lady
A Rich Aunt
An Important Person
The Lady of the House
A Friend

EPILOGUE

SCENE

The same, and yet not the same. The tables and chairs are as before—the worn carpet, the three-branched gaselier. But the room from a dingy boarding-house parlour has become a pleasant, homelike place. A little furniture polish, a little soap and water, has accomplished wonders. Some one with a sense of art has redraped the windows, changed some of the pictures on the walls, hunted out some bright "Sheffield plate" for the sideboard, redecorated the gaselier, supplied spring flowers in old china vases. Not so much money as loving care has been spent. Good taste, among other things, would seem to have entered into the house since last we saw it.

[*It is again a foggy Friday afternoon, and again* MRS. SHARPE *sits at the desk, making out her bills—a pale, thin lady who during the interval has grown a good many years younger. The lines of fret and anger have disappeared—a gentle, somewhat shy lady with a habit of smiling to herself. She is dressed in a quiet, dark frock with lace shawl. It, maybe, is a little old-fashioned, but it suits her. The widow's cap is of another pattern—and colour. Her spectacles lie on the desk near to her hand.* STASIA *enters, carrying a tray laden with tea-things, which she proceeds to spread over a dainty tea-cloth. The china and the silver make a bright picture very different to the untidy jumble of the first Act.* STASIA *is a neatly clad, fragile-looking little person, her dark hair in soft folds each side of the somewhat pallid face with its large, wistful, childish eyes. A slight fit of coughing seizes her after she has laid down the tray. She waits a while to recover her breath.* MRS. SHARPE, *turning her head, looks at her.* STASIA *smiles.*]

MRS. SHARPE

[*Turning again to her work.*] You don't get rid of that cough of yours.

STASIA

It's only these fogs. I'll be all right when the sun comes.

MRS. SHARPE

Shall pack you off to the seaside for a month if you don't get rid of it soon.

STASIA

[*Looks up from her laying of the table.*] Pack me off! For a mon——! [*Laughs contemptuously.*] A nice muddle I'd find everything in when I got back.

MRS. SHARPE

[*Laughs.*] Don't you be so conceited—thinking nobody can get on without you. How many candles have you had for Mr. Wright this week?

STASIA

Six.

MRS. SHARPE

[*Looks up.*] Six? I thought it was four.

STASIA

Let me see. There's the pair on the mantelpiece. Then one—no, you're right. 'Twas only four.

MRS. SHARPE

I thought I only recollected four. [*Writes.*]

STASIA

I was counting in the two left over from last week. [*From the sideboard drawer she has taken the afternoon apron and cap. The former she has put on, the cap she is now fixing.*] Haven't got a pin, have you?

MRS. SHARPE

[*Examining the pin-cushion of her chatelaine.*] I don't think—yes, I have, just one.

[STASIA *has come over and kneels down.* MRS. SHARPE *is "fixing" the cap.*]
You needn't wear it, if you'd rather not. It's only a custom.

STASIA

Oh, I think it gives tone to the house. I don't see anything to be ashamed of in it. I rather think it suits me.

MRS. SHARPE

[*Looks at her. Then, smiling, pats her cheek. The girl rises.*] Why didn't Miss Kite come down to lunch?

STASIA

Said she wasn't feeling hungry.

MRS. SHARPE

Not ill, is she ?

STASIA

She's fretting herself.

MRS. SHARPE

[*After a pause.*] I am sorry for her. She'd be really a nice-looking woman if it wasn't for——

STASIA

Would you mind my talking to her ?

MRS. SHARPE

You !

STASIA

You see, if anybody else was to say anything to her it might hurt her. I'm only a little servant-girl that she needn't even listen to, if she don't want to.

MRS. SHARPE

You think it could be of any use ?

STASIA

She only wants a little courage put into her.

MRS. SHARPE

Very well—try.

STASIA

I'll make the tea, and then——

[*The door opens. Enter* JAPE SAMUELS. *The oiliness, the aggressiveness, have disappeared. The cunning has gone out of the face; it is seen to be rather a handsome face with its chiselled nose, its high forehead. The moustache has been shaved off, the thick hair brushed back.*]

SAMUELS

Good afternoon! [*To* STASIA] How'th the cough? [*His lisp remains, but somehow it is no longer objectionable.*]

STASIA

[*Indignant.*] What cough? Everybody talking about me as if I was some bedridden old woman, past her work. Haven't got a cough!

[*She goes out, pulling the door sharply. The gong is heard a little later.*]

MRS. SHARPE

I've been threatening to send her off to the seaside. It has made us a bit short-tempered. [*Laughs.*] You are home early.

SAMUELS

Friday is always a short day in the City—for us Jews. [MRS. SHARPE *looks at him.*] Is that my bill? [*He is by desk. Takes up one of the bills.*]

MRS. SHARPE

[*Glances at it.*] Yes.

SAMUELS

You've made a mistake.

MRS. SHARPE

Have I?

SAMUELS

Chop on Wednesday you haven't charged me for. [*Gives it her back.*]

MRS. SHARPE

I had forgotten. [*Leaning over the desk, she adds the item.*] Will you be leaving us?

SAMUELS

Why should I?

MRS. SHARPE

Well, you've referred once or twice of late to the fact of your being a Jew. I have been fearing——

SAMUELS

It isn't what he eats and how it's cooked that makes the Jew. It wasn't the manna, it was the Ten Commandments that led us out of bondage—welded us into a people. [*His voice has taken a fine ring; a fine look in his eyes.*] Will the "salon" be well attended this afternoon? [*Smiling.*] It *is* the third Friday, is it not?

MRS. SHARPE

[*Laughs.*] Yes. Yes, I think everybody will be here.

SAMUELS

It was a delightful idea.

MRS. SHARPE

It is foolish of me, perhaps. But it brings back old times. [*With another nervous little laugh*] I like to imagine—if only once a month—that you are all my guests.

SAMUELS

Your guests always. [*He takes from her hand the receipted bill.*] We pay you—little enough—for the accommodation of a boarding-house. [*He slips the coins into her hand.*] Your thoughtfulness, your kindness, have given to us a home. Your bill still leaves us in your debt. [*She gives him a grateful smile.*]

[*Opening the door, he finds* VIVIAN *on the point of entering. He draws back, holding the door open for her. She enters, passing him with a smile and bow. They exchange a "Good afternoon."* VIVIAN *carries a bouquet of early hyacinths.*]

VIVIAN

You are running away from us?

SAMUELS

To return more worthy of my company. [*Smiles. He goes out.*]

VIVIAN

I am the first?

MRS. SHARPE

And therefore the most welcome. [*Kisses her.*] How is your mamma?

VIVIAN

She's got a slight headache. She'll be down in a few minutes. [*She is near the sideboard.*] Shall I put these in water ?

MRS. SHARPE

They are my favourite flowers.

VIVIAN

[*She fixes the flowers in a bowl with water, and brings them to the table.*] I heard you say so on Sunday. She worries herself about papa. The more cheerful he is, the more she persists in regarding it as a cloak concealing an aching heart. [*Laughs.*] As a matter of fact, he is doing remarkably well, and is naturally pleased with himself.

MRS. SHARPE

I suppose she dislikes the idea of his having become a commercial traveller. I can understand it.

VIVIAN

I can't. I've just been having it out with her.

Why shouldn't a gentleman do useful work for which he has special qualifications?

[*The door opens, the* MAJOR *puts in his head.*]

MRS. SHARPE

[*Laughing.*] We are talking about you.

MAJOR

[*Entering, hat and cane in hand.*] I am honoured.

VIVIAN

I was saying how fitted you were to be a commercial traveller.

[MAJOR *winces.*]

VIVIAN

[*She goes up to him.*] You are not the poor fellow that gets shown the door. [*She is touching up his hair.*] Nobody dares to be impertinent to so fine a gentleman.

MAJOR

[*Laughing, well pleased.*] Well, yes. I suppose manner and bearing [*draws himself up*] do——

VIVIAN

Why, it's taken even me quite a long time. [*Kisses him.*]

MAJOR

[*He takes her hand in his.*] My dear, if——

[*Enter* STASIA *with tea and a plate of muffins, which she places.*]

MAJOR

[*Seeing her, breaks off and turns to* MRS. SHARPE.] It was, to tell you the truth, Mrs. Sharpe, about that little bill transaction of ours that I looked in.

MRS. SHARPE

Oh, don't let that worry you.

MAJOR

I have instructed my bankers to take it up—on Tuesday.

MRS. SHARPE

It is very kind of you. You are sure——

MAJOR

The kindness, dear lady, has been yours—throughout. [*He goes out.*]

[*Outside he meets* MRS. DE HOOLEY. *They are unseen, but their conversation is heard—or rather partly heard.*]

MAJOR

Ah, good afternoon! And how do we find ourselves this afternoon?

MRS. DE HOOLEY

Oh, just so-so. Your lumbago, I trust, Major, is better.

MAJOR

I thank you—a little.

MRS. DE HOOLEY

So glad.

[*The* MAJOR *goes his way upstairs.* MRS. DE HOOLEY *enters the room.*]

MRS. SHARPE

[*Greeting her.*] How *are* you, dear?

MRS. DE HOOLEY

How are *you*, dear?

[*They kiss.*]

What do you think of it? [*She stands and turns*

for them to inspect her new dress. It is a simple dress of poor material, but it has points.]

MRS. SHARPE

[*After a pause.*] I think she's *going* to be clever.

MRS. DE HOOLEY

It's absolutely her first attempt, you must remember. [*To* VIVIAN] How do *you* like it, dear?

VIVIAN

[*Joining them.*] Is that the frock your sister has been making for you?

MRS. DE HOOLEY

Yes. Of course, she's got a lot to learn.

VIVIAN

I like the way she's cut the skirt.

MRS. SHARPE

If she can cut a skirt well, that's everything.

STASIA

[*Unnoticed, has approached.*] I like that little bow on the shoulder.

MRS. DE HOOLEY

Do you know, I think it *does* help.

STASIA

Looks so saucy.

MRS. SHARPE

[*Playfully pushes her towards door.*] Here, you take yourself off. And don't forget those muffins.

[STASIA *goes out.*]

MRS. SHARPE

I should say she would do well.

MRS. DE HOOLEY

I've taken a place for her in Judd Street. It's a bigger rent than I intended, but then, it's so handy for the 'buses.

MRS. SHARPE

She must be very grateful to you, I'm sure, dear.

MRS. DE HOOLEY

Well, you see, dear, there's the children. Four of them, and really——

[*There enters* JOEY WRIGHT *with* CHRISTOPHER.

WRIGHT *is a tubby, kindly-looking little man, with small twinkling eyes. So much of his appearance as a man himself may be deemed responsible for has been altered for the better.* CHRISTOPHER *is the same, except that hope and enthusiasm have taken hold of the boy. They enter talking and laughing. The women break up.* MRS. SHARPE *goes to the tea-table.* MRS. DE HOOLEY *and* VIVIAN *remain talking.*]

MRS. SHARPE

[*As she turns away from them.*] We shall all do what we can, dear. [*She crosses and greets the two new-comers.*] How is the picture getting on ?

CHRISTOPHER

We were just discussing a point.

WRIGHT

What do you think he wants to do ? Paint me as a friar.

CHRISTOPHER

Don't you think it would be a good idea ? [*Taking* MRS. SHARPE'S *lace shawl from her shoulders*, *he drapes it as a cowl round* WRIGHT'S *head.*] "A Friar of Orders Grey."

MRS. SHARPE

[*Laughs.*] You are quite right. He does make an excellent monk.

CHRISTOPHER

[*He replaces the shawl round* MRS. SHARPE'S *shoulders. She is pouring out tea.*] We will try it to-morrow. I'll have the dress ready. [*To* MRS. SHARPE] Can I help?

MRS. SHARPE

[*She hands him two cups of tea.*] Yes. You can say something pleasant to Mrs. de Hooley about her frock.

CHRISTOPHER

What an extraordinary——

MRS. SHARPE

I didn't ask you to criticise it. I asked you to say something pleasant about it. I'll tell you why afterwards.

[CHRISTOPHER *laughs. He crosses with the cups.*]

[MRS. DE HOOLEY *and* VIVIAN *are near the piano,* MRS. DE HOOLEY *sitting,* VIVIAN *standing.* CHRISTOPHER *joins them, and they talk together. Occasionally a few words are heard, for instance:*]

VIVIAN

What do you know about it? [*With a laugh.*]

[CHRISTOPHER *having been expressing views concerning* MRS. DE HOOLEY'S *dress.*]

MRS. DE HOOLEY

But, my dear, an artist——

WRIGHT

I want you to do me a favour. As soon as he's finished with me, I want you to let him paint you!

MRS. SHARPE

I should like it immensely, but I'm afraid I can't afford——

WRIGHT

Don't be silly. You don't think I mean you to pay for it. We'll have it over the mantelpiece in the dining-room. I'm tired of looking at myself in a mirror that makes me out twice as broad as I'm long.

MRS. SHARPE

[*Understands, and she smiles at him.*] What a good fellow you are! [*She has risen to greet her new guest.*]

[LARKCOM *has entered, a cheery young blade, dressed in a grey frock suit, clean-shaven, his hair somewhat long and "artistically" arranged.*] How did the concert go off?

LARKCOM

[*He has developed a theatrical manner, which rather suits him. He is fond of the centre of the stage and of gestures.*] The greatest success I have *ever* achieved.

CHRISTOPHER

A good house?

LARKCOM

[*He shrugs his shoulders.*] The house—might have been better. But the enthusiasm!—the enthusiasm! That new song of mine! I could have been singing it now.

[*Between the others an amused smile passes.*]

MRS. SHARPE

[*Who, having shaken hands with* LARKCOM, *has returned to her duties.*] You will be glad of a cup of tea.

[SAMUELS *has entered—in changed dress.*]

SAMUELS

Well, how did it go off?

LARKCOM

My boy——

[MRS. SHARPE *hands him his cup of tea.*]

LARKCOM

Thank you. There was *one* man, in the second row——

SAMUELS

Only one!

[*The* OTHERS *laugh.* LARKCOM, *putting down his cup, seizes a knife.* JAPE, *laughing, places himself the other side of the table.*]

MRS. SHARPE

[*She holds out to* LARKCOM *the empty hot-water jug.*] Hand that down the stairs to Stasia, will you ? for some more hot water. I don't want to give her the trouble of coming up twice.

LARKCOM

[*Taking the jug.*] You think one jug will be sufficient among so many ?

MRS. SHARPE

[*Laughs.*] Don't you be impertinent.

[LARKCOM *goes out.*]

MRS. SHARPE

I'm ashamed to say I've never heard him—except, of course, here of an evening. I never seem to get the time. [*She is replenishing cups which* CHRISTOPHER *has brought over.*]

WRIGHT

Oh ! he's good.

SAMUELS

Not as clever as he thinks himself. [*With a laugh*] I suppose one could say that of all of us. But he's worth hearing.

MRS. SHARPE

I must really try.

[*The* MAJOR *and* MRS. TOMPKINS *have entered.* MRS. SHARPE *rises and greets them.*]

Sorry to hear, dear, that you've got a headache.

MRS. TOMPKINS

Oh! it's all right now. I think it must be his coming home that has taken it away. [*With a laugh*] They say one trouble will always drive out another. [*She gives a little squeeze to his hand.*]

MAJOR

[*He fetches and places a chair for her.*] You bear witness, Mrs. Sharpe, I am compared to a headache.

MRS. SHARPE

[*Who has reseated herself; she laughs.*] You are very badly treated.

[*The* MAJOR, *making himself generally useful, hands some bread and butter to* MRS. SHARPE, *the muffins to his wife. Later he joins* VIVIAN *and* CHRISTOPHER, *and laughs and talks with them.* LARKCOM *has re-entered with jug of hot water.*]

LARKCOM

[*He brings it over to* MRS. SHARPE.] Couldn't

find Stasia. I took it the hot water was the essential thing.

MRS. SHARPE

Thank you very much.

[MRS. DE HOOLEY *has joined the group at the tea-table.*]

MRS. TOMPKINS

Is that the sister's frock ?

MRS. DE HOOLEY

Yes. I thought——

MRS. TOMPKINS

I want you to give me her address, dear. I'll tell you what I've been thinking——

[*They sink their voices.*]

MRS. SHARPE

[*Handing a cup to* JAPE.] Sorry to have kept you waiting.

SAMUELS

[*He takes it with a "Thank you." He has been talking to* LARKCOM.]

[STASIA *has appeared at door.*]

STASIA

May I speak to you ?

MRS. SHARPE

[*She hands a cup of tea to* MRS. TOMPKINS, *and then joins* STASIA *by the door, where they whisper.*]

WRIGHT

I say, Samuels, what's become of that silver-mine of yours—in Ireland ?

SAMUELS

Do you still want to be in it ?

WRIGHT

Well, is it any good ?

SAMUELS

As a silver-mine—— [*snaps his fingers.*] As a dairy-farm—might be a good sound investment.

WRIGHT

A dairy-farm ?

SAMUELS

Take a run over with me on Monday, see what you think of it.

WRIGHT

Thanks, I will.

SAMUELS

With a good manager—everything up-to-date——

MRS. SHARPE

[*Coming down.*] If you please—everybody.

[ALL *turn towards her.*]

Miss Kite—— [*To* STASIA.] Just keep a look out——

[STASIA *stands with the open door in her hand.*]

MRS. SHARPE

Miss Kite is on her way downstairs. [*Her air and tone of mystery claim attention.*] The question is, how are we going to receive her ?

MRS. TOMPKINS

Why—what ?

MRS. SHARPE

It will not be the Miss Kite we have hitherto known. It will be a new Miss Kite. According to Stasia, a pale-faced, middle-aged lady with brown hair—a little thin on the top.

[*A movement and a silence.*]

MAJOR

[*Striking the table with his hand.*] Speaking for myself, I shall like her better.

MRS. TOMPKINS

[*Laughs.*] I think we all shall.

MRS. SHARPE

She'll be terribly nervous, poor lady! We must make it as easy as we can for her.

MRS. TOMPKINS

Well, I shall congratulate her on her good sense.

MRS. DE HOOLEY

I think, with perfect truth, we shall be able to tell her it is an improvement.

LARKCOM

Take my advice, you'll say nothing.

MRS. TOMPKINS

But surely she'll expect us——

MRS. SHARPE

Do you know, I'm inclined to agree with Harry. I know I should myself. I should rather nobody took any notice.

CHRISTOPHER

I think that's right.

MRS. TOMPKINS

Well, if you all think so.

SAMUELS

That's the right idea. She's a sensible woman. She'll understand.

STASIA

I think I heard her door.

MRS. SHARPE

Go out through the dining-room.

[STASIA *goes out through the folding doors.*]

Then that's settled. [*She slips back to her place.*]

MAJOR

That's right.

SAMUELS

[*Turning to* WRIGHT.] She'll be more grateful

to us for silence than for anything we could say.

WRIGHT

We can just be nice and pleasant to her. Let her feel that——

[*There enters* MISS KITE, *a quietly dressed, middle-aged, pale-faced lady, but good-looking. Her thin brown hair tinged with grey is parted in the middle and neatly arranged each side of her face.* MRS. SHARPE *is busy with the tea.* MRS. TOMPKINS *and* MRS. DE HOOLEY *are talking dress.* WRIGHT *and* SAMUELS *are discussing the farm.* LARKCOM, *by desk, is talking to* VIVIAN. *The* MAJOR *and* CHRISTOPHER *have hastily plunged into Art.*]

MAJOR

[*Whose voice is always easily heard above that of the others.*] What I say about Velasquez is this—— [*He stops as* MISS KITE *enters.*]

MRS. SHARPE

[*Rising, she goes to* MISS KITE. *Kisses her.*] So glad you have come, dear.

MRS. DE HOOLEY

[*She is standing close by.*] We should have missed you so much.

MRS. TOMPKINS

[*From her chair.*] We always look to you for our conversation.

MISS KITE

[*The poor lady is in an agony of nervousness. Her voice is uncertain.*] Thank you. I'm afraid my conversation this afternoon—— [*She is on the point of breaking down.*]

MAJOR

[*Placing a chair for her.*] Won't you be seated?

MISS KITE

[*It is in a central position. She hesitates, looking about her, frightened.*] Thank you. I——

LARKCOM

[*He notices her desire to keep her face turned away as much as possible from every one. With rapid explanatory pantomime to the* MAJOR*—who, grasping the idea, smiles and nods—he places instead one of the easy-chairs in front of the fire, where she* *can sit apart.*] Wouldn't you rather be nearer the fire ?

MISS KITE

[*She gives him a quick, grateful glance.*] Thank you. I don't know whether it is my fancy, but it does seem to me to be a bit chilly this afternoon. [*She sits.*]

WRIGHT

[*He brings over and places a footstool.*] We good people have got to take care of ourselves.

[MISS KITE *turns to him with a smile.*]

CHRISTOPHER

[*He has brought over tea on a tray with the et ceteras.*] Cream or milk ?

MISS KITE

It's so kind of you. [*Helping herself with trembling hand, she spills the milk.*] I'm so sorry. I seem so clumsy.

CHRISTOPHER

[*He wipes her dress with his handkerchief.*] I don't think it will mark. Luckily it was only the milk.

SAMUELS

[*He brings her a plate of small cakes.*] Take my advice, try one of these. [*He returns to his talk with* WRIGHT.]

[STASIA *has entered with fresh muffins.* VIVIAN *brings one over to* MISS KITE. *She places it on the right arm of the chair, and stooping, whispers* :]

VIVIAN

You are looking so nice.

MISS KITE

[*She looks up at the girl. She cannot speak. She draws her nearer and kisses her.*]

[VIVIAN *returns the kiss, then slips away.*]

MISS KITE

You are all of you so kind, I—— [*The tears begin to come. She takes out her handkerchief.*]

[*They have appeared to notice nothing. A sympathetic smile has now and then, perhaps, passed—a whisper of instruction or advice. The idea has been to put her at her ease, as far as the difficulty will permit. They talk as before among themselves, laughing, moving here and there.* CHRISTOPHER *has joined* VIVIAN *again.* SAMUELS *and* WRIGHT *are talking. The* MAJOR *has joined them.* MRS. SHARPE *is in her place at tea-table.* MRS. DE HOOLEY, MRS. TOMPKINS, *and* LARKCOM *form a group near her.* STASIA *is on her way out.*]...

SAMUELS

[*Raising his hand.*] Listen!

[*From the foggy street, faint at first, growing fuller, rises the voice of a singer. The words are in strange tongue, but the sweet voice fills the little room with its music.* STASIA *pauses.* MISS KITE *dries her eyes. The listening faces lighten.*]

MRS. SHARPE

[*After a silence, to* CHRISTOPHER] Open the window. [*To the women*] Do you mind? Do you mind, Miss Kite?

[*They answer " No," " I should like it, " Please, do."* CHRISTOPHER *goes to the lower window, opens it. The sound of the voice comes clearer.*]

MRS. SHARPE

Who is it ?

CHRISTOPHER

[*At the window.*] There is no one.

MRS. SHARPE

No one ?

CHRISTOPHER

I can see no one.

MAJOR

Must be in some other street.

[*The song dies away.* CHRISTOPHER *closes the window.*]

MRS. SHARPE

It sounded to me like a child's voice

CHRISTOPHER

I thought it a woman's.

VIVIAN

Hark ! I hear it again.

MRS. SHARPE

It is further off.

SAMUELS

Some beggar, I suppose. Poor fellow!

[*They listen. They have turned towards the window.*]

[*The door opens.* THE STRANGER *stands there as in the Prologue, with hat and staff in hand.*]

[*None at first see him, except* STASIA. *He makes a sign to her; she remains silent. The voice dies away. He puts aside his hat and staff.*]

MRS. SHARPE

[*She turns and sees him.*] Ah! [*She goes to him, smiling.*] You come at the end of the feast.

THE STRANGER

[*Smiling.*] It is when friends feel kindest towards one another.

MRS. SHARPE

[*She laughs.*] I was beginning to be afraid—— [*She pauses.*]

THE STRANGER

Afraid?

[*The others return to their talk.* MISS KITE *alone remains seated.*]

MRS. SHARPE

I never feel quite sure how long—— [*Laughs.*] You know you told me, when you came, you were but a Wanderer.

THE STRANGER

[*Smiling.*] But then I was a Stranger—and now a Friend.

MRS. SHARPE

Yes. But we lose our friends.

STRANGER

Ah no. They are with us always. [*She looks at him.*]

SAMUELS

[*He comes to them—holds out his hand to* MRS. SHARPE.] I have some letters to write before the country post goes out. [*He shakes hands with her, then turns to* THE STRANGER.] You do not happen to be looking for a sound investment? [*Laughs.*] If so—I'm turning my silver-mine into a dairy-farm.

THE STRANGER

You think that the more profitable?

SAMUELS

The more profitable. Though maybe [*with a smile*] I'd have made more pounds, shillings, and pence out of it, but for you, sir. This fellow, Mrs. Sharpe, [*They are near the table,* MRS. SHARPE *has returned to her duties*] has a trick of leading a poor devil into extravagant tastes—love of one's good name, desire for the honour of one's people. Such things cost dear, in the City.

THE STRANGER

It is the mission of the Jew—to teach the Law. You remember the words: "Ye shall be unto Me a kingdom of priests, an holy nation." A great inheritance, though, as you say, sir, may be somewhat costly to maintain.

[MRS. SHARPE *has poured out a cup.* STASIA *brings it to* THE STRANGER *together with a plate of cakes or small biscuits. He takes it with a smile of thanks—eats and drinks.* STASIA *waits, watching.*]

SAMUELS

[*After a moment.*] You have always taken it for granted, sir, in all our conversations that I was a fine fellow, in sympathy with fine ideals. But that is not what surprises me : it is to find —that you are right. [*Smiling.*]

THE STRANGER

[*He has taken but a bite and sip—has handed the cup back to* STASIA.] Yes. And this is what we will tell to the young men—that the fear that keeps men little is the fear of being great.

SAMUELS

[*He looks at him.*] Yes. We will tell it to the young men. Good-bye.

THE STRANGER

[*Taking his outstretched hand.*] Good-bye.

[SAMUELS *goes out.*]

[MRS. DE HOOLEY *is talking to* LARKCOM. WRIGHT *is with* VIVIAN *and* CHRISTOPHER *by piano,* MISS KITE *in her chair by the fire,* MRS. SHARPE *at head of table. She is piling up the tea-things on tray.*]

MAJOR

We also, Mrs. Sharpe, must be going. [*Checking her reply.*] Mrs. Tompkins is of opinion that a little dinner—[*He turns to his wife; they smile at one another*]—at the restaurant, followed by the theatre would be a fitting complement to a delightful afternoon.

[*Leaving his wife to say a few words to* MRS. SHARPE, *he comes to* THE STRANGER.]

I have Mrs. Tompkins's commands, sir, to ask you to join us.

THE STRANGER

[*He negatives the suggestion.*] You know the old proverb.

MAJOR

"Two are company, three are none." Ah, yes. But with you, sir, somehow, it seems different. We cannot help feeling that it was you, sir, who—without knowing it—brought us together again. [THE STRANGER *listens. The* MAJOR *glances round, sinks his voice.*] Mrs. Tompkins and myself, before you came, had not—had not been getting on as well together as—as perhaps we led you to believe. [*He glances at* THE STRANGER, *but the grave, quiet face is unreadable.*] My fault, sir—my fault.

THE STRANGER

[*Smiling.*] It is always " our " fault.

MAJOR

[*He laughs. With a glance again towards his wife.*] Children, sir—that's all they are, just children. [*Confidentially.*] Maybe sometimes a little trying. A gentleman should always remember to be gentle with them.

THE STRANGER

[*He lays his hand upon the* MAJOR'S *arm.*] Remembering all our promises to them, even to the foolish ones, for our own Honour's sake.

[*The* MAJOR *looks at him ; he is smiling. There is a moment's pause.* MRS. TOMPKINS *joins them.*]

MRS. TOMPKINS

It has just occurred to me, John. [*She gives his neck-tie a little twist of rearrangement.*] May not Vivian think it unkind, our going out and leaving her ?

MAJOR

[*He glances across at the group at the piano.*] Do you know, I really don't think——

MRS. TOMPKINS

[*Smiles.*] Perhaps not. But she may be hurt at our not asking her.

MAJOR

We will find out how the land lies. [*He joins the group at the piano.*]

MRS. TOMPKINS

You are coming with us ?

THE STRANGER

[*Again he puts aside the invitation. Smiling*] You shall be content with one admirer.

MRS. TOMPKINS

You confess yourself that ? [*Then more seriously.*] Thank you. It is of so much help to a woman to have an admirer—[*she looks up at him with a smile*]—one who thinks well of her, who expects from her—her best.

THE STRANGER

You see, I have known you—so long.

MRS. TOMPKINS

Not all the time, I'm glad to think. We women

forget it is our privilege to be the "Better Half"—the more forbearing. You men are such good creatures—[*laughs*]—if only we remember you are nothing more than just big boys.

THE STRANGER

Ah, yes. The whole round world—what is it? But Woman's child, claiming from her tenderness.

MAJOR

[*Returning.*] It is all right. Quite a coincidence. Young Christopher was only waiting to ask our consent to his taking Vivian out to dinner this evening.

MRS. TOMPKINS

And you gave it?

MAJOR

It seemed to just fit in.

MRS. TOMPKINS

[*Half acquiescing, half despairing.*] I suppose you know he hasn't a penny.

MAJOR

My dear! He has a cheque for fifteen pounds.

He showed it me. Has sold two pictures in one month!

MRS. TOMPKINS

[*She laughs and shrugs her shoulders.*] Well! [*Turning to* THE STRANGER] So you will not come?

THE STRANGER

You shall place an empty chair for me—between you.

MAJOR

My dear, we will. He shall be our guest, if not in body, then in spirit. Good-bye, sir.

THE STRANGER

Good-bye. A pleasant evening.

[*The* MAJOR *goes a little way towards the door.* MRS. TOMPKINS *does not immediately follow. He stands waiting.*]

MRS. TOMPKINS

[*Her eyes on* THE STRANGER.] It is odd. I remember you so well—— But never the time—the place. It is as if we had met—in dreams.

THE STRANGER

And so much of life is dream. It is a good meeting-place.

[*She joins the* MAJOR. *He opens the door for her. She turns with one last look to* THE STRANGER, *then passes out. The* MAJOR *follows her, closes the door.*]

[LARKCOM, *leaving* MRS. DE HOOLEY *with* MRS. SHARPE, *comes to* THE STRANGER.]

LARKCOM

[*Smiling.*] Got a bone to pick with you, sir. You have never been to see my show.

THE STRANGER

You are sure?

LARKCOM

You—you mean you have paid?

THE STRANGER

You think it was not worth it? [*Smiling.*]

LARKCOM

[*Shakes his head.*] I didn't want you to do

that, sir. The whole thing was your idea. I have always looked upon you, sir, as my partner.

THE STRANGER

I shall always regard it as a title of honour. [*His hand is on the boy's shoulder. He looks at him.*]

LARKCOM

[*Taking out his book and pen, and writing.*] Any time, sir, any place—you just come in—take your seat. [*He gives* THE STRANGER *his card, repockets his book and pen.*] I don't think, sir, you will find anything in it to make you ashamed of the connection. "Fun without Vulgarity": that's my motto.

THE STRANGER

It could not be better.

LARKCOM

[*Holding out his hand.*] And thank you again for having revealed to me that I was an artist!

THE STRANGER

[*Taking his hand, smiling.*] And Philanthropist?

LARKCOM

Well, if taking pleasure in giving pleasure, irrespective of how much is in the house, is philanthropy—[*smiling*]—yes, sir.

THE STRANGER

Ah!

[MRS. SHARPE *is about to carry out the piled-up tray.*]

LARKCOM

Shall I take it down?

MRS. SHARPE

Well, it is——

LARKCOM

[*He takes it and, crossing with it, pushes open with his foot one of the folding doors. Then turns.*] Don't forget—at any time—in any place.

THE STRANGER

[*Smiling.*] Thank you—Partner.

[LARKCOM *goes out.*]

[MRS. SHARPE *is busying herself putting all things in order.*]

[THE STRANGER *has remained standing near the fire.* MRS. DE HOOLEY *comes to him.*]

MRS. DE HOOLEY

I wonder, do you take any interest in women's frocks ?

THE STRANGER

[*Smiling.*] Why not ? Women are of so much importance, and a woman's frock of so much importance—to a woman.

MRS. DE HOOLEY

[*Laughs.*] Tell me, what do you think of it ? My sister—she thought she would like to be a dressmaker.

[MRS. SHARPE, *busy with her affairs, goes out, leaving the door partly open.*]

This is her first production.

THE STRANGER

I think it a beautiful frock.

MRS. DE HOOLEY

You like it ?

THE STRANGER

It becomes you.

MRS. DE HOOLEY

I shall be so glad if she succeeds—for the children's sake. I quite look upon them as my own. [*Then in another voice*] We women are poor things without children.

THE STRANGER

And there are always children.

MRS. DE HOOLEY

[*She nods.*] Rather fortunate, is it not ?—for lonely old women. [*She goes on quickly*] To tell the truth, I was getting a bit tired of being the poor relation. It is pleasant finding oneself for a change—[*she looks up at him, smiling*]—the rich aunt.

THE STRANGER

Ah ! you have learnt it : that all the best fun in life is—Giving.

[*Laughter comes to them from the group by the piano.*]

MRS. DE HOOLEY

Yes. It is good fun. You will come and see them one day—will you not ?—my children.

THE STRANGER

One day. I promise.

MRS. DE HOOLEY

[*Pausing on her way; she turns again.*] Remember.

THE STRANGER

One day, I promise.

[*She goes out.*]

[THE STRANGER *turns.* MISS KITE *has risen.*]

MISS KITE

You see, I have grown vain.

THE STRANGER

You have excuse.

MISS KITE

You still think me beautiful?

THE STRANGER

I think you beautiful.

MISS KITE

[*She comes to him.*] I understand. All men

and women are fair. Only so many of us disguise ourselves in all manner of ugly colours.

THE STRANGER

All men and women are fair. And some are fairer than others. And they shall be the kinder, having the more to make them kind.

MISS KITE

[*Smiling.*] To which do I belong ?

THE STRANGER

[*He also is smiling.*] Your glass shall tell you.

MISS KITE

[*Laughs.*] You are determined I shall be vain.

THE STRANGER

Of your rightful place among fair women.

MISS KITE

[*She looks at him.*] It is curious. Your voice conjures up to me always the same picture : of an elfish child, with her chin upon her knees, asking questions of the fire. [*Thinking, she shakes her head.*] I see only the little rounded back, like a note of interrogation.

THE STRANGER

The little wistful face was very fair.

[*She gives him her hand. Then, in silence, she goes towards the door; turns, smiling, then goes out.*]

[WRIGHT *and the* LOVERS, *talking, have drawn nearer.* WRIGHT *comes forward.*]

WRIGHT

You have not been up to see my portrait.

THE STRANGER

[*Turns.*] It is finished?

WRIGHT

All but the drapery. Should rather like you to see it.

CHRISTOPHER

[*Laughs.*] The fact is, sir, we are quarrelling about the price. We thought that, perhaps, you might be able to decide between us.

WRIGHT

I want to pay him what it's worth to me. That's business.

CHRISTOPHER

He wants to pay me—well, [*laughs*] I won't say more than it's worth—but more than I would get from any one else. I can't accept, can I? It would be——

THE STRANGER

A gift. And no man may accept a gift with honour—save from a friend.

[*A silence.*]

CHRISTOPHER

It isn't that, sir. He is a friend—[*he puts his arm shyly round the old man's shoulders*]—a dear friend. That's why I can't bear the thought of imposing upon him.

WRIGHT

Who's imposing? I know what I'm about. I'm not a picture-dealer. I'm an Art Patron [*with his trick of pointing to himself*]. Always thought I'd like to be an Art Patron. I'm going to brag about it, later on, that it was I who discovered you.

CHRISTOPHER

[*Laughs.*] I seem to be in an awkward position.

THE STRANGER

You have a partner. And in business, when one is in an awkward position—[*smiling*] you see, I know all about it—one leaves it to the partner. She shall decide. [*He turns to her.*] Whether it shall be price, such as stranger pays to stranger—or gift, that we may take with honour only from the hands of those we love.

VIVIAN

[*She comes forward, gives to the old fellow both her hands.*] Yes. Let it be gift. [*She draws nearer to him, smiling into his eyes, kisses him.*]

WRIGHT

[*The old fellow is taken aback. The tears come into his eyes. He turns away. After a moment, from over his shoulder, he speaks to* THE STRANGER.] Should you like to see it—one day—when you've got the time. Clever bit of work. [*He sinks his voice—jerks his thumb in the direction of* CHRISTOPHER.] Wonderful sense of colour—quite wonderful. [*He passes out.*]

[*A silence.*]

CHRISTOPHER

[*He looks toward the open door through which old* WRIGHT *has passed.*] How is one to know people? I used to think him such a bad man. [*Laughs.*]

THE STRANGER

[*Smiling.*] "The business of Art is to reveal the beauty underlying all things."

CHRISTOPHER

[*To* VIVIAN] They were his words—my Master, who first taught me. [*He turns to* THE STRANGER] How I wish he were still here among us! How you would have liked one another!

THE STRANGER

You have given up—"trying to forget him"?

CHRISTOPHER

I am trying to remember him, sir, how much he expected of me. [*He puts his arm round* VIVIAN, *draws her towards him.*] We are going to do good work—whether it pays, or whether it doesn't. We have discussed it all thoroughly so that we shall not be taken by surprise like—like other people are. We are going to be prepared for everything—even for poverty.

THE STRANGER

Ah ! that is the secret. Love ! she is a woman. And all men can she love—save one ; with all men may she dwell—save one : with all men save the coward. It is not poverty ; it is the fear of poverty that drives out Love.

[*A moment.*]

CHRISTOPHER

[*He holds out his hand.*] Good-bye, sir. I am glad you came into this house. I cannot tell you all you have done for me. It would not sound much—in words. I wish there was something we could do for you, in return.

THE STRANGER

You would ? [*He is between them. He lays a hand on each.*] It will seem so easy. But there will come days when the memory of a promise made to a friend may help. You shall give me, as a gift, this promise : that through all things to the end you love one another.

[*The fog is thickening. The light struggling through the twin windows is faint and yellow. They move towards the doors. A white hyacinth, fallen from the bowl upon the table, lies upon the floor.* VIVIAN, *stooping, picks it up, holds it pressed between her folded hands. One feels that often in the years to come she will take it from its secret place ; that, gazing at it, she will see again the fading room,* THE STRANGER *standing with bent shoulders.*]

[*They turn their eyes again to* THE STRANGER, *his face is towards them. They pass out, smiling, through the open door.* MRS. SHARPE *has entered through the folding doors. She stands watching. They pass out without seeing her.* THE STRANGER *turns. She comes towards him.*]

MRS. SHARPE

You are going away from us : something tells me. Ah no ! do not answer me : do not let me know. It is only for a little while. You will be returning—very soon. Your room will be ready for you—always.

THE STRANGER

[*He, smiling, holds out his hand.*] As friends, at eventide, we will merely say Good-night.

MRS. SHARPE

[*Smiling, she takes his hand.* Good-night.

[*She turns. Upon the shining mahogany table stands only the bowl of hyacinths. A few drops of water are spilled. With her handkerchief she wipes them away. At the folding doors she turns again, smiling.*] Good-night. [*She passes out, closing the doors.*]

[THE STRANGER *stands silent. After a while the door opens again.* STASIA *enters.*]

STASIA

[*She goes to the sideboard, opens it, takes out the tablecloth.*] Still keeps foggy, don't it ?

THE STRANGER

[*Her eyes are bent upon her work. He stands before her.*] I see blue skies and sunshine.

STASIA

[*She looks up. He is looking into her eyes, smiling.*] You mean me ? [*She laughs.*] Yes, it doesn't matter, does it ? [*She lets fall her work, flings her arms about him.*] Oh, it was such a muddle before you came—life ! everything ! I couldn't make head or tail of it.

THE STRANGER

There are so many cannot make head or tail of it.

STASIA

[*Still with her arms about him.*] And all the while it is beautiful. [*The clock on the unseen mantelpiece strikes the half-hour—two strokes. She unclasps her arms.*] Time does fly, doesn't it? [*She goes to take up the cloth again.*]

THE STRANGER

[*He stays her.*] There is something I want you to do for me. Come to the door with me. Leave-takings are but wasted sadness. Let me pass out quietly. Close it softly behind me.

STASIA

[*A dumb pain is taking hold of her.*] You must go?

THE STRANGER

I also am a servant. I have my work.

STASIA

[*She conquers herself—drives back her tears behind smiles. She puts out her hands to him.*] It was so kind of you—to come.

THE STRANGER

[*He takes her in his arms.*] I came because you wanted me.

[She goes to the door with him, opens it. He does not turn his face again. She stands with the door in her hand till beyond the misty square he passes from her sight. Then very softly she closes the door.]

[She comes back slowly into the quiet room, goes to the table, smooths out the folded cloth, takes it up in her hands. She has left the room door open. Through the fanlight steals the sunshine. It lies, a beam of light, across the room. Turning, she sees it. She goes to it. Her arms stretched out each side of her, she raises her face so that the sunlight, bathing her face, kisses her parted lips. So she stands a while, her face framed in the light. Then she takes up again the folded cloth, goes with it through the folding doors. And the face that passes out is the face of one to whom Love itself has spoken.]

[The stage remains empty. The bowl of hyacinths upon the shining mahogany table. The shaft of sunlight falling on the worn carpet.]

THE CURTAIN FALLS

Printed in Great Britain by Hazell, Watson & Viney, Ld.,
London and Aylesbury.